Giving Birth, How it Really Feels

SHEILA KITZINGER is Britain's foremost childbirth educator and is also a social anthropologist studying birth, breastfeeding and motherhood in different cultures.

After studying social anthropology at Ruskin and St Hugh's College, Oxford, she went on to research and teach at the University of Edinburgh and wrote her M.Litt. thesis on race relations in Britain.

Sheila Kitzinger's studies on the contemporary culture of childbirth include research on induction of labour, episiotomy and women's experiences of hospital care. Her anthropological studies include research on the Rastafarian faith and on sex, pregnancy and birth among Jamaican women (working with the Medical Research Council at the University of the West Indies) and, with an award from the Joost de Blank Research Fund, research on the problems of West Indian women and their children in Britain.

She is known in many countries as a writer, lecturer and teacher on the social and psychological dimensions of birth, parenthood and motherhood. She lectures widely and publishes in Britain, Scandinavia, Australia, South America, Germany, Italy, Israel, the USA and Canada. She has studied methods of childbirth education and the management of labour in places as far afield as Mexico and East Germany. Sheila Kitzinger is on the Advisory Board of the National Childbirth Trust and the Advisory Committee of the Midwives Information and Resource Service, chairs the Foundation for Women's Health Research and Development and is a Consultant to the International Childbirth Education Association. She was awarded an MBE in 1982 for her services to education for childbirth.

Sheila Kitzinger's books include *The Experience of Childbirth*, *The Experience of Breastfeeding*, *The New Good Birth Guide*, *Pregnancy and Childbirth* and *Woman's Experience of Sex*.

She is married to Uwe Kitzinger, President of Templeton College, Oxford. They have five daughters. The family home is outside Oxford.

Giving Birth, How it Really Feels

SHEILA KITZINGER

Victor Gollancz Ltd
London · 1987

To Uwe

An earlier version of this book, called *Giving Birth:*
The Parents' Emotions in Childbirth, was first published
by Victor Gollancz Ltd in 1971.

Giving Birth, How it Really Feels first published
in Great Britain 1987 by Victor Gollancz Ltd,
14 Henrietta Street, London WC2E 8QJ

First published in Gollancz Paperbacks 1987

British Library Cataloguing in Publication Data
Kitzinger, Sheila
  Giving birth: how it really feels.
  1. Childbirth
  I. Title
  618.4′092′2   RG651

  ISBN 0-575-04110-2
  ISBN 0-575-04111-0 Pbk

Typeset by Centracet
Printed and bound in Great Britain by
Biddles Ltd, Guildford and King's Lynn

Acknowledgements

I should like to thank all those women who have shared with me their diverse experiences of birth, in long, fascinating letters and lengthy phone calls. I have been privileged to learn from them. From every one I have gained fresh insight and understanding.

None of my books could have been written without the other women who support me. I want to thank Judith Schroeder, my secretary, who creates order out of chaos on my desk and shares the excitement I feel about the work we are doing. And my thanks – warm and heartfelt – go also to Hazel Wilce, who cleans the house and creates order out of chaos there with her tremendous energy and efficiency.

S.K.

All photographs are by Nancy Durrell-McKenna, except pages 87, 149 and 161 by Kathryn Berry.

Contents

Birth: A Personal Statement of Belief

Childbirth is often seen as a medical crisis and pregnancy as a pathological condition which must be terminated by delivery in an intensive care setting. The task of the obstetric team is to 'treat' the patient and to actively 'manage' the labour with all the sophisticated technology at their disposal, including ultrasound, continuous electronic fetal monitoring, intravenous catheters and the surgical scalpel, so that the product of pregnancy, like any product, leaves the factory in the best possible condition. And what happens after that is nothing to do with the obstetrician.

I believe that birth need not and should not be like this. Only for a small minority of women – not more than 10 per cent – is it necessary to 'manage' childbirth in this way. Obstetric intervention should be restricted to those labours in which there is obvious malfunction and where the baby is clearly at risk. To be able to predict which these are is what obstetrics should really be all about. Whenever intervention takes place it should follow discussion and be a shared decision between a fully informed woman and those helping her. There ought to be a great deal more openness and honesty about obstetric practice and midwifery routines and nothing should be done to a woman, however kindly, and however good the intention, unless she has consented to it and understands the possible effects and side-effects for her and the baby. Every woman, however 'high risk' she is considered to be, should be cared for in a spirit of service, with respect for her individuality, with courtesy, consideration, gentleness – and love.

To make the process of bringing new life into the world one in which the woman is treated as if she were merely the container for a fetus – a passive patient being delivered, rather than an active birth-giver – is to degrade and violate her.

It is often taken for granted that anyone engrossed in the study of the birth experience must be pronatalist and believe that all women should want babies and be enabled to have them, whatever the obstacles. I cannot agree with that point of view. There are many other satisfying kinds of life, and myriad ways of personal fulfilment. I want women to explore all the possibilities of development and to resist being cast into the mould of mothers unless that is what they really want. I hope women will grasp the reins of power, and turn that power into an energy and life-enhancing force which is very different from the kind of power that men have wielded throughout history.

Birth, like death, is a crisis, but one which can also be a developmental experience for those sharing in it. As the great stream of humanity flows through life these are times for drawing closer together, for reaching out to each other in love and compassion; not for withdrawing and surrendering ourselves to whatever 'science', and a medical system which takes no account of human emotions and human needs, superimposes on us. At the depths of both experiences, in spite of pain, there is a fierce joy. Death leads us to thanksgiving for all that a person has been. In a similar way, birth is a celebration of life. Both are more than biological events. They express human values.

After a baby is safely born it must be reared. The experiences through which both parents have passed, the preparation for their new roles and for the demanding relationship with even the most adorable child, affect the way in which they are able to respond to that challenge. We have created a style of childbirth in the developed countries in which birth is an interruption of normal life rather than an integral part of its flow. We have taken it outside the home and away from the family – so that for a couple having a baby it may come as a great surprise that birth has anything to do with loving and, for the woman, that it can be a profound psychosexual experience.

Traditionally in human culture, birth has been a satisfying and personally fulfilling achievement for a woman. A mother still has added status in most Third World societies, and other women – neighbours, family members – support her and share in the rites and comforting which help her over the bridge into motherhood and through the psychologically and socially difficult period in which she is in a state of 'becoming'. In our own culture we ignore or trivialize this kind of emotional support and sharing between women. Many doctors dismiss our concern about the emotions of childbearing as just 'the icing on the cake'.

Doctors focus on perinatal mortality statistics. Women, too, want their babies born alive and healthy. But obstetricians often treat women as if they did not care about their babies – only their own emotions. Yet the person who most cares what happens to a baby, whose thoughts are focused on it, whose whole life is moulded around this child-to-be, is no one on the obstetric team. It is the mother.

Increasingly, obstetricians have been forced by pressure from women to aim to 'satisfy the consumer', as if they were running a supermarket and had to provide the goods most in demand in order to keep their customers. This has made for some improvements in care. There are now, for example, birth rooms with sprigged wallpaper, flowery curtains and soft music, and beds with backrests and squatting bars. Some time-honoured practices like enemas and shaving the perineum, decking every-one out in sterile garments from top to toe, keeping women lying flat on their backs in labour, and separating mothers from their newborn babies, have been phased out because they have proved useless and even dangerous.

But a fundamental change in attitude is necessary. Women, after all, are not 'consumers'. They are producers. They give birth to babies. The commercial model is an unsuitable one. We need instead to develop a model of care based on a sense of community of service to support the natural process of birth and respond to women's needs.

We are only now discovering the long-term destructive effect on human beings and families of treating women as if they were merely containers, to be opened and relieved of their contents; and of concentrating attention on a bag of muscle and a birth canal, rather than relating to, and caring for, the person to whom they belong. The violence which is a common element in childbirth today leaves many women feeling that birth has been a kind of rape. This sort of experience is not easily forgotten. It can shatter a woman's self-confidence, make her doubt her ability to mother her baby, destroy joy in the expression of her sexuality, and attack her very sense of self – the roots of her identity. It is psychologically mutilating.

11

The nearest thing I know to the atmosphere of a room where birth takes place, in which the woman is given quiet encouragement and emotional support to follow her own instincts and to allow the creative force to sweep through her body, is the silence of a Quaker meeting which has truly 'centred down'. Those present are sharing in an unfolding of life, waiting on it without haste, and opening themselves to it.

There is a great deal of discussion today about 'bonding' of mother and child, and concern to provide an opportunity in the moments after delivery for her to get to know her baby and feel it hers. But this process is not a magic chemistry which can be forced on mother and child in an alien and uncaring environment. It is not surprising that some women withdraw from their babies. Their own needs are too great. Everything that happens after delivery is the outcome of preceding events. Bonding can either be facilitated or made very difficult by the atmosphere in the birth room, and the interaction of those in it.

The culture of childbirth in our society is important for all of us because the way we give birth is not only, or primarily, a medical matter. It is a matter of our deepest values, of the quality of relationships between human beings, and of the kind of society in which we want to live – and which we create for those who come after us.

Sheila Kitzinger

PART ONE

Birth as Experience

The urgent questions that women ask about childbirth mostly stem from one basic one: *'What is it really like?'* – 'What do contractions feel like?' 'How shall I know when labour has started?' 'How much will it hurt?' 'How long does the first stage last?' 'When shall I go to the hospital or call the midwife?' and so on. Since labours vary so much, it is difficult to answer any of these queries with accuracy, but if vague generalizations are proffered instead women feel, quite rightly, that the answers are irrelevant and evasive. That is why this book focuses on the rich variety of human experience in childbirth. What some women enjoy, others dislike. Sensations which bring pleasure to some are frightening or distressing for others. The unfolding pattern of childbirth can vary widely too, so that for some women labour is all over and the baby delivered inside a space of a few hours, while others labour right through the day and night and are still not fully dilated.

When women talk to each other they are often reticent about describing how they really felt in childbirth. They hold back on communicating the power and immensity of the experience, because they are anxious not to alarm others who have not yet 'been through it'. I find that it is sometimes very difficult in childbirth classes to stimulate discussion about previous labours – especially ones that were difficult – for this reason. It means that some women, pregnant for the first time, come to childbirth unaware of its intensity and sometimes not facing up to the fact that many labours are painful and that most, even when straightforward, have a pain period at the end of the first stage which can be very difficult to handle.

There are other women who describe with apparent relish each ache and pain and who flaunt obstetric difficulties as if they were rosettes, prizes for having suffered in labour, to be exhibited proudly in front of those who have not yet been put on trial. It often seems to me that pregnant women attract horror stories of this kind because they grow up knowing very little about the subjective experience of birth, however much they may have studied the anatomy of the rabbit and diagrams of female reproductive organs. Very few of us have had the opportunity as children of actually being present at a birth. It may be that we have missed out on an important educational experience. Childbirth has been medicalized, sanitized, taken out of the home. It has become a process managed by professionals within the isolated hospital environment.

The 'old wives' tales' often told to pregnant women provide in Western culture a kind of initiation into adult womanhood by warning women of possible dangers and suffering to come, rather as initiation rites in tribal society involve the use of terrifying masks and ordeals to mark the threshold of adult status.

'Old wives' tales', says the Oxford Dictionary, are 'trivial stories, such as are told by garrulous old women'. It is significant that no one ever talks about 'old husbands' tales' or 'old doctors' tales'. Women are blamed instead. It is implied that there is poison in their speech and that the only safe thing for them to do is to remain silent. The experiences that women share with other women are thus rejected and trivialized.

Doctors and midwives often urge their patients not to listen to 'old wives' tales'. I have even heard an obstetrician advise patients never to talk to other women at all about childbirth. I believe that this is entirely wrong. We need to share our experiences, not to spread horror stories, but to know what labour is really like as a subjective experience and to learn from other women who have faced the challenges ahead of us. In fact, many expectant mothers and new mothers are socially isolated. They have friends and work colleagues who have not yet started their families and who tend to be interested in different things. If a woman goes on working till the seventh month she may find that she faces childbirth in three months' time knowing very little and with no one to talk to about it.

In reality it is not other women who instil and fuel anxiety in most pregnant women, but the medical care system itself. In many hospitals, the whole atmosphere of care during pregnancy, and everything that happens in the antenatal clinic, stresses the risks of childbirth. Indeed, doctors sometimes warn women that childbirth is 'only normal in retrospect'. The medical approach to childbirth is risk-oriented and, even when lip service is paid to childbearing as a major life experience rather than a medical event, in practice screening in pregnancy and all the potent ceremonial procedures of hospital birth are focused on pathology.

Even the childbirth class can reinforce this sense of danger if it concentrates on techniques and technology and does not provide sufficient opportunity for free discussion and for hearing from other women at first hand what labour feels like.

Obstetrics have changed dramatically over the last 35 years. New machines and technical procedures detect with more precision deviations from normality. The norm is defined in terms of a statistical curve, the partogram, to which labour is expected to conform. Though a margin is allowed on either side of the curve, the actual size of this margin is decided by the obstetrician, so that some permit only two hours' variation in the speed of dilatation of the cervix, whereas others allow four. Few women are allowed to have long, slow labours nowadays, even if they are happy with them. Few are allowed a gentle, protracted lead into labour. The emphasis is on the uterus as an efficient working mechanism which gets cracking on time and operates at top speed and power. Everything else is considered abnormal and merits intervention. The clinical experience of midwives about the very wide variety of births and the labouring woman's own feelings are now considered unimportant compared with the record of the partogram. A good servant has become a bad master and an undoubtedly useful tool has come to dominate childbirth.

Treating birth as if it were a pathological event rather than a normal life process has an effect on all those working professionally with childbearing women as well as on the women themselves. By concentrating almost exclusively in the training of obstetricians and midwives on the diagnosis and treatment of malfunction and disease, and on intervention to avoid it, our society has succeeded in producing professionals many of whom have never seen a natural birth and who know nothing of the skills of supporting the normal physiological process. It is important for those working in maternity care to understand labour also as women experience it and this is much more subtle than just saying 'It's painful' or 'It's painless'. So I hope that medical students and pupil midwives will feel that there is something in this book for them too. Account after account tells of the things that helped women in labour and of what they found important at the time and reveals their hopes and fears so vividly that they convey with more directness than any textbook a great deal about the psychology of childbirth.

It is important that neither partner approaches this book as if it could show a woman how she 'ought' to have a baby. Here are first-hand accounts of women's experiences during the exciting journey of discovery which is labour, a journey which is unique for each person venturing on it. In these accounts I have tried to select reports which do not necessarily tell of easy labours, but which reflect the personalities of the writers: some 'feet on the ground' – practical, unemotional and matter-of-fact; others passionate, totally involved and caught up in a drama of Wagnerian magnitude.

I believe that this is one of the important things about preparation for childbirth – that it should not simply superimpose a series of techniques, conditioned responses to stimuli, on the labouring woman, but that it can be a truly creative act, in which she spontaneously expresses herself and the sort of person she is.

Education for birth consists not, as some would have it, of 'conditioning', but aims at giving a woman the means by which she can express her own personality creatively in childbirth.

There is no such thing as a 'textbook labour'. Each one is different, and brings its own problems, challenges, satisfaction and joy – in much the same way that a marriage which may be superficially like any other marriage, is a unique relationship between two unique people. Education for childbirth and parenthood involves not only exercises and explanations, intellectual information and physical training, but – ideally – an emotional awakening which brings with it increased self-realization and deeper understanding of a whole network of human relationships extending from a partnership and a family into the surrounding society.

Nor is it my intention to suggest that it is only births for which the mother has had previous antenatal instruction that can be happy. By chance or temperament, or because they are physically healthy, a great many women have fairly quick, efficient and non-traumatic labours. Others have careful preparation but labour turns out to be difficult and painful.

Prepared childbirth offers no magic formula. It may be 'natural' or 'unnatural', depending on whether extra obstetric help is needed, can be long or short, difficult or easy. Sometimes a forceps delivery or a vacuum extraction will be necessary – sometimes a Caesarean section. The point is that either way the woman in labour is co-operating with her own body and with her obstetric attendants to give birth to a live, healthy child, and she can do this better because she is acting with understanding, fearlessness and control.

This book is written not only for expectant mothers, but for men too. Having a baby is a joint enterprise, and there are a good many things about a pregnant woman that a man can never begin to understand if he does not take time to think about what her pregnancy and the coming baby mean to her, and some of the inner experiences through which she may be passing, as well as the events of labour, and what she can learn to do to be 'in tune' with her body during the processes of dilatation and expulsion.

Whoever is going to be a woman's companion in labour needs to learn how to help her and to understand what kind of help she thinks she wants. The support person can learn much of this in childbirth classes – how to rub her back, tell her she is doing well, place a sponge soaked in ice water at her lips. But it is not just a matter of having coaching techniques. It is difficult to know exactly what you want until you are caught up in the experience and it is for real. There are a great many other things described in these pages that couples have discovered by chance were right for them at the time. It is important for a birth companion to be flexible and sensitive to what the woman wants, and yet strong, so that when she enters the stress period of the late first stage he or she can be her anchor in a stormy sea, giving emotional energy and unflagging support, and sharing each contraction with her.

The point of education for birth is that childbirth becomes not something that simply happens *to* a woman, in which the question of how to cope with pain is paramount, but a process in which she actively and gladly expresses herself. It is not a performance to be enacted, nor an examination that must be passed, but is a profound and all-enveloping experience in which she opens herself to the creative power of the uterus. It is here that the great distinction lies between the incidental pain common to most labours, and suffering. For suffering in childbirth is an anachronism nowadays. With good preparation beforehand and loving support at the time, and with the additional aid of modern drugs for pain relief if necessary, no woman should have to suffer in labour. Instead it becomes an exciting adventure that brings with it a sense of deep satisfaction, thrilling achievement and triumph.

Nevertheless, many women looking ahead to labour worry that childbirth pain will prove too much for them, and that they will somehow 'give way' and reveal their true selves. The implication is that our 'real' selves are nastier than the images we ordinarily present to the world – and that we require a sort of mask to hide the unpleasantness of our inner natures. But it is this real inner self, capable of the heights and depths of emotion, which is also the self which can relish the excitement, drama and tumult of labour and the intensely moving and passionate experience of bringing new life into the world. For many women who are bearing a child, sex is associated with intense pleasure and when they make love they express their feelings spontaneously through their bodies without needing to think of doing exercises or achieving some standard of performance. Undrugged childbirth is an overpowering experience in exactly the same sort of way as sex. A woman is completely caught up in the passionate act of creation, utterly committed to the feelings of the moment and to the vivid sensations with which her whole being is flooded. She may not look as if she had just powdered her nose or been to the hairdressers. But with eyes shining and cheeks flushed, and hair damp and tangled, she is beautiful in exactly the same way as she is when she is sexually aroused.

Nor will she behave in a way any different from her normal personality. If she quickly gets impatient or frustrated and cross, or tends to be argumentative, or if she anticipates trouble long before it occurs and 'crosses her bridges before she comes to them,' or if, on the other hand, she becomes quickly flustered and panics when things happen for which she is not prepared, these aspects of her personality will find expression also in the way she acts in labour. If she is not on very good terms with her body and thinks it rather inefficient or unlikeable, this attitude too she will carry over into her labour – and she will not really trust it to work properly.

If a woman is obsessional about always doing the right thing, or proving to her parents that she is not a failure, she may face labour, too, in an obsessional way. She feels that she must be a success and may have a rigid idea of how her labour ought to be. If all does not go as planned she has 'failed'. If she is dependent on her mother she may well carry over this dependence on to the midwife or obstetrician. If she is the sort of woman who intellectualizes everything and lives 'in her head', she will probably try to gain control over her labour in the same way, and may be disturbed and uneasy when she discovers that the sensations of childbirth sweep through and involve one's whole body and being, and cannot be isolated in the brain or completely controlled by the intellect. If she has been socially conditioned to be unassertive in everyday life and dare not stand up for herself or set limits on what other people do to her, she is also likely to be unassertive in labour and find it difficult to say 'no' firmly and persistently when obstetric intervention is proposed.

Because most of us have been brought up to be yielding, and to think of submissiveness as an attractive feminine characteristic, this is one reason why, when confronted with the power of medicine, we often feel as if we have been pushed on to a conveyor belt, unable to question what is being done to us or protest effectively.

For childbirth is not something separate and apart. It is something which *involves characteristic responses*, even though the context of action involves a unique creative activity.

In preparation for childbirth we need approaches which are fluid enough to adapt to different women's personalities and the varied choices they make. Some women will always want not to 'be there' – and simply to go to sleep and wake up with a flat tummy and a pink bundle in a cot. And if this can be made a truly safe method for both mother and baby – which it really is not – then a woman should have the right to make this decision for herself and to have her baby this way. Others want to know something of the drama of childbirth, but without the intensity of feeling which is nearly always involved in unmedicated labour; they may prefer some form of regional anaesthesia in which they are paralysed or numbed from the waist down, with epidural anaesthesia. When women seeking a natural birth need obstetric assistance an epidural may be one of the best ways of enabling them to participate and experience the joy of birth.

Others feel that all the sensations of normal labour: the tug and tussle of dilatation of the cervix, the back-ache and thigh-ache and tummy-ache, the enormous stretching feelings, the pressure of the baby's head as it is eased through the birth canal, and the slippery ecstasy as the little body is at last released and swims out into the world, limbs lashing in freedom – that all this, even though it involves discomfort and probable pain, and acute sensations which are more powerful than anything else one has ever experienced, is infinitely worth while. These are the women who say, 'Please let me try to do it myself', and who may be far too busy to be bothered with analgesia or injections because they are completely wrapped up in the task of giving birth, and in responding with carefulness and concentration to the stimuli coming from the uterus. Compassion and understanding on the part of those attending such women in labour consists not primarily in offering pain-relief, but in helping them do, as far as lies in their power, what they set out to do, by giving encouragement, the information they need in order to be able to make choices between alternatives, and emotional support.

The women in these pages tell how birth really was for them and what other people did to help them. After reading just a few of these accounts no reader could conclude that adjustment to labour is simply a matter of breathing and blowing at the right time, or of getting the right breathing level, or having sufficient techniques of distraction at your disposal.

There must be very few women who go through labour with

a clear picture, like a diagram from an obstetrics textbook, of what is occurring in their bodies. This is just as well. Birth is a psychosexual experience, not simply a medical event. In sex, too, anatomical information gives way to fantasies about the flowing, growing, enveloping self, and perhaps the more that we can surrender and simply *let the body be* without directing it, the more satisfying the lovemaking. Some women describe their labours in terms of what happened and what they did; others draw on this extra dimension of being, the fantasies with which they were flooded and which make of the many different sensations of labour a unique pattern and a coherent whole in the imagination. I believe that the capacity for rich and positive fantasy enriches birthing as much as it does lovemaking and that just as the vagina seems to burn, merge with another being and dissolve in sex, so the fantasies about contractions, sensations in the birth canal and the fanning out of perineal tissues as the baby comes to birth contribute towards harmonious psychosomatic activity and the rhythmic co-ordination of breathing and body as the whole self is caught up in and focused on one imperative, urgent, creative act.

For me in my own labours this has always been expressed in terms of imagery of water and its movement. I have felt gathered up on waves as contraction has followed contraction with relentless power, and the birth of the baby has come as if on a tide which streamed through me.

The wave surges toward me, rises in crescendo as I am enveloped by the walls of its pressure, and then sweeps back and away, leaving my body bounded by the little space, the utter peace and content, between contractions. The uterus works mechanically like the heart, without my willing or dictating what it shall do. Its muscle fibres contract and constrict – feel as if they must grind and pulp, like a ripe peach pressed till all its juice pours out, and everything in the deep well of the pelvis is squeezed and trodden as if in a wine press.

It comes again, with controlled power. Go with it. Breathe with it, up and over. The big contractions are the *good* ones. Skim over each, brushing the wings of pain. Soar above the raging waters, the swelling wonder of creation as the womb-fruit ripens, tilts, and feels almost bursting in its strength:

bigger than any other muscle in the human body, or the biceps of a champion boxer. The contraction fades, the wave washes back. Down the slope into peace, the two minutes in which my boat is beached before it must set off again into the storm.

The waves come faster, and I must go towards each with measured pace, keeping above them with my breathing. If I try to turn and run away, they will engulf me. Each one bears in the tide, brings it sweeping in – the great flooding waters of birth. The gates of the body open as the baby is pressed down the arc of the birth canal, head moulded by its confines. My body is like an island fretted by waves, like a widening bay filled by the swollen tide. My cliffs and beaches are relentlessly eroded; the channels run with the foaming water, hot in its torrents. Leonardo's cataclysm was formed from waves like these but these bear life on them, not death.

The widening bay turns warm, prickles with heat, as the tide urges toward it. My body has become a vessel from which life is poured. The child's head, like the hard bud in the middle of the peony, pushes forward between all the uncurled, spreading petals. Wait, as the flower opens. Feel the top of the baby's head with wondering fingers, the soft down of the hair, and wait for the next surge; gently ease it forward.

The pod pops. Like a seed bursting, the head slides through and slips out, sweet and smooth, eyes tightly closed, face puckered in displeasure at the world. Shoulders slither out, arms flailing, finger fronds uncurling, rib cage working, tough little thighs and heels thudding, knees churning – my child's body glowing pink – and her mouth opens in a roar as, with a tearless cry, she greets life with innocent rage.

In one sense preparation for childbirth is 'medical', if only because pregnancy and labour involve physiological changes which are supervised by medical personnel, and assisted when necessary. But in another sense preparation is working through *feelings*, and concerns emotional aspects of adjustment to a phase of life, a different image of the self, and a different social role. In this sense it is not 'medical' at all, and calls on teaching and counselling skills, on techniques derived from group dynamics, and insights and research in the fields of psychology, sociology and social anthropology (personally I would add the advantages of training in acting too). Childbirth education is impoverished and drained of much that it has to offer once it is restricted to mere anatomy and physiology, relaxation drill and breathing techniques. And, unfortunately, in many clinics throughout the country shortage of time, understaffing, and lack of opportunity for further training on the part of those doing this work, mean that this is the picture often presented. Childbirth education is really a new profession, which needs a specific combination of skills, special qualities of personality, and a certain sort of previous experience, which is different again from that of the midwife or physiotherapist.

Many of the women whose stories are recorded here had been to classes and used special types of breathing, neuro-muscular release, massage, postural variations and techniques of gaining increased comfort. The actual exercises they did and the responses they rehearsed beforehand are described in my books *The Experience of Childbirth** and *Pregnancy and Childbirth*.† Very often they added adaptive responses of their own, and this was encouraged in my classes. I have learned a good deal from my students who have experimented in this way, and have often incorporated what they taught me into my teaching.

The basic idea is that instead of fighting her body, trying to escape from pain, the woman in labour responds positively with conscious and rhythmic breathing – varying with the phase of labour – and with skilled relaxation which comes from an awareness of what happens to her body under stress and from knowing how to 'switch off' tension. It is rarely that a woman is able to do this completely with all contractions, but there is always a rest period, however short, between contractions, which allows her to gain complete release of tension and to prepare for the next contraction. The use of these 'bridge periods' between contractions is most important, and especially so in the fierce storm that terminates the first stage.

Moreover, everyone attending classes knows that if she feels the need there are additional pharmacological aids which she is perfectly justified in using, not 'instead' of her relaxation and

* Pelican (6th edition), 1987.
† Penguin, 1986.

breathing but in addition to them. It is not a question of 'either/ or', but of the intelligent co-ordination of available techniques which seem to suit that particular labour and that particular woman.

But for a woman to feel free to do this, teaching should not merely present an ideal standard of behaviour in labour which she tries to attain. It somehow has to give her the self-confidence and trust in her body which enables her to *incorporate* that ideal, so that it becomes part of herself and feels the natural and spontaneous way to behave. 'It seemed the obvious thing to do' . . . 'The breathing came quite easily. I didn't really have to think about it' . . . or even 'I had a shot of pethidine and I just went straight on breathing and relaxing, and dozing between contractions'. It is only too easy to fall short of this and to teach in a way that means that a woman goes into labour determined with all her might and main to have a labour like someone else she has heard of or read about, to 'do the exercises', to 'live up to' her teacher, or to prove something about herself. When this happens it looks as if teaching has been efficient up to a point, but has been communicated more as a series of skills than as an art. For this is the basic distinction between techniques – like piano scales or dance steps or the isolated actions of the skier practising on dry land – and an art in which all these actions are co-ordinated and synthesized into a whole, which, because it looks so easy and smooth, seems absolutely 'natural'.

Every childbirth educator knows of women who can do all the isolated 'drills' perfectly and who are shining examples of how to do it to the rest of the class. They know too that these may well be the women who have the least happy labours and who are unable to adapt themselves to the stimuli coming to them from the uterus. It was all in the head and not in the body; this is partly the result of the whole process of the intellectualization of a natural process which has come about through the movement for preparation for childbirth, and especially through psychoprophylaxis. Childbirth becomes more an academic exercise, or even a circus act, like a dog jumping through a burning hoop.

So there may be something to be said for 'natural childbirth' after all, a term which is now more or less taboo among childbirth educators, if not among the general public. But prepared childbirth is natural not because it teaches women that they can go out and squat in the woods with the squirrels and other wild creatures and have their babies on a pile of leaves, or that they do not need doctors and midwives or antenatal care, or that it 'shouldn't' hurt and that they have done something wrong or are unworthy if it does – but rather that the end result of careful training and of self-understanding is the co-ordinated psychophysical harmony which appears natural.

Reading these accounts, it becomes obvious that great flexibility in approach and techniques is necessary if a woman is to have the best opportunity of adjusting to any sort of labour. The one who only has a rigid training, and who is taught to do so many breaths a minute or to breathe at a special level when she is so many centimetres dilated, or who is instructed to breathe in and out twice and then hold her breath for a count of ten with second stage contractions, *may* find that this drill suits her labour perfectly, and happens to harmonize with the type of contractions she encounters. But she is more likely to discover that this blueprint does not fit her particular labour, and that, however disciplined her conditioned responses, she has sacrificed the chance of achieving true psychophysical co-ordination by being trained to react without feeling. It is almost as if we are sometimes frightened of the tremendous and overpowering surge of physical and emotional sensations in labour, and as if we are afraid of being 'undisciplined' and caught up in this great tumultuous sea of uterine contractions. Some sorts of antenatal drill are like learning a series of incantations, a magical device, which will ward off evil and suffering if only we repeat it consistently and mechanically. And, of course, this *may* work, and provide effective distraction from pain. 'Raising the pain threshold' the Pavlovians call it. But it is a poor second to really going 'with' your labour and responding sensitively to the stimuli of contractions like an orchestra obeying the conductor. And occasionally, it must be admitted, these carefully learned exercises seem utterly irrelevant to a particular labour, and the woman feels she is lost on uncharted seas. This is where two things can help her: firstly, the mental flexibility, self-awareness and courage to explore the possibilities of adapting and modifying techniques to suit her specific needs; and secondly, encouraging labour support which offers guidance not in terms of how labour 'ought' to be, but of how it actually is for her, as well as accurate information on the progress of labour.

This is where a birth companion who has shared in her prenatal preparation is of untold help, and, especially in a difficult labour, can give that vital extra emotional support that permits her to get over the top of the really huge waves of contractions at the end of the first stage.

It is because childbirth cannot be reduced to a succession of exercises that support at the time of labour, and companionship and encouragement, are very important. Most women need someone there who understands what they are trying to do, and who is able to help them and in some way to share the experience with them. Many have been unable to have this and have still enjoyed their labours, but the optimum emotional climate for childbirth is one in which all are working together with understanding and co-operation. So in this respect, too, childbirth is not just a series of exercises; it is also a venture in human relations. This aspect has often been ignored. The pregnant woman has been taught how to recognize the various phases of labour, what her attendants may do, and how she should behave. But she has not learned how to understand what is going on in the minds of her attendants, why they tend to act in a certain way, or how to communicate to them what she wants. This may seem to demand too much of the woman in labour, but unless it can be explored she embarks on labour with the risk of social disorientation and isolation, enduring a 'solitary confinement', while wondering what 'they' will think, what 'they' will do to her, and even – worst of all, if 'they' will 'interfere'.

What does it feel like to be a midwife when your patient is only 4 cm dilated and breathing away like mad? Or when she simply seems to be working too hard and you are sorry for her? Or when it looks as if you are useless and as if she wants nothing to do with you or any help you can offer? What pressure is a midwife under when she has had strict instructions not to allow a woman to be in the second stage of labour for longer than 45 minutes and knows that if she calls the obstetrician a forceps delivery will then be done? How does a midwife feel when she has avoided an episiotomy because the woman said she did not want one but there is a perineal tear for which she feels personally responsible?

It is important for antenatal classes to explore human motivation and conduct in the labour ward. Because this is so often the great rock on which women who have had training founder when actually in labour. It is only by putting oneself in somebody else's place, and by an act of imagination achieving understanding, that one can really develop a strategy to negotiate effectively.

Through understanding the way the medical system works, awareness of the stresses and strains in relations between doctors and other staff and the ways in which power is exercised in hospitals, and with knowledge about midwifery routines and protocols, a woman has the basis on which to be assertive and to make informed choices between alternatives. Not knowing about these things means that she is rendered powerless in childbirth. The choices women are offered are then spurious. For information is power. Without it a woman is merely at the receiving end of whatever care other people decide to give her and whatever trivial choices they permit her to make. To be able to keep control in labour a woman has to have some understanding of the medical system in social and political terms and not struggle merely to gain personal concessions and plead with individuals to be allowed to do things her way. This is a subject which needs to be explored in childbirth classes, and to do so effectively teachers themselves need to understand something about the sociology of the medical care system.

The father of the baby or a close woman friend is often the best person to give labour support. A 'significant other' who really knows the woman is more likely than any professional to understand how she is feeling. He or she knows when tension is building up before it is apparent to anyone else, has ways of giving her strength and the right words with which to infuse in her new confidence and courage.

We should not take it for granted that the labour companion

must be the father of the baby. For many women that will be the person they choose. Others want another woman with them. Certainly in a Lesbian partnership it is important for the other woman to be fully involved in the pregnancy and the preparations for birth. They are both enriched by this and it is a vital element in the enormous transition to loving and taking on the responsibility for a new life and in giving each other mutual support in their changing roles.

Some women dismiss the possibility of support from a male partner, however, simply on the grounds that he is 'not the type'. In that case, maybe it is time he learned. The most unlikely men are marvellous during labour. A man who, for example, his wife asserts, 'said "Oh horrors!" whenever the baby was mentioned', not only stayed with her during the birth but cradled her in his arms as their baby was born. Many men have been astonished at how much they had to give, at how much they were needed, and were fascinated and enthralled by birth – when they always thought of themselves as squeamish and readily alarmed by blood and nauseated by female biological processes.

A labour companion should have the opportunity of sharing in preparation in order to understand what is happening, anticipate what is to come, know how to refresh, encourage and nurture the woman and have a meaningful part to play in the drama. This includes giving verbal encouragement and loving touch, helping her be mobile and to change position frequently, and offering firm physical holding. Sometimes, too, it entails standing back, because that is what she wishes, and letting her get on with it. Like a skier at the top of a mountain or a swimmer confronted with huge waves, there are times when the woman can only tackle the challenge alone. She wants to know there is strong support in the background but anything the other person tries to do to help will be intrusive. She needs *space*.

This does not mean that the partner is extraneous. The very fact that this person does not panic when labour starts, wanting to rush her to hospital immediately, is confident in recognizing the signs of the late first stage and in reassuring her that she is doing well and that everything is fine, and can convey love in whatever way is appropriate, may profoundly affect the way a woman feels about and handles her labour.

It is most important that the birth companion has a constructive part to play and is not simply a 'hanger-on' and 'voyeur' of the scene of labour. Especially in a 'high-tech' obstetrically managed labour, professional attendants may make a companion feel a non-participant onlooker who is likely to get in the way. The machinery and apparatus can seem much more relevant to the situation than loving human help. But this is not so. Technology is not good at supporting the normal physiological process. Far from increasing a woman's confidence and helping her get in tune with her body, it often shatters confidence and causes her to doubt her ability to give birth. This in turn is followed by physiological changes in blood flow, oxygenation, muscle tone and breathing which have an adverse effect on the progress of labour and reduce the oxygen which is essential for uterine contractility and which flows in the feto-maternal circulation. One reason why this happens is that when a woman feels in harmony with her body in a labour that is going well, endorphins – mood-elevating and pain-relieving natural opiates – together with other hormones (one of the most important of which is oxytocin) which gives power to the uterus and assists muscle coordination, are spontaneously released into her bloodstream. They play an important but still inadequately understood part in labour and in protecting the mother and baby. Human love expressed in touch, tenderness and intimacy can get all these hormones flowing. No machinery has been invented which can do it.

The birth companion has a vital part to play and it is never just a matter of watching. Being with a woman in labour when you are unable to help, but are simply expected to observe what she is going through, can be a traumatic emotional experience. This is why inaction can be painful for doctors, too. They often intervene in labour because of their own feelings of anxiety. Thus labour can be complicated not only by fetal distress and maternal distress, but also by obstetrician's distress.

A man may be anxious because he has heard the apocryphal stories about men who faint. Some doctors have a fine line in tales of this type: 'And he had to be treated for concussion' . . .

'The mother and baby were fine but we were afraid we'd lost him.' It is true that occasionally a man feels sick or giddy and has to sit down or go out of the room because he is over-whelmed by stimuli. Even more rarely he passes out. In my experience these are the men who feel helpless in a situation for which they are inadequately prepared, which they cannot comprehend, and which is fraught with tension and drama. Denied action, all they can do is to retreat from the disturbing situation and faint.

I remember a man who was an habitual fainter, and would pass clean out if he cut his finger and saw blood. We discussed whether he should risk being present. He decided to take a chance, and simply to walk out if he felt queasy. Should he faint, doctor and midwife agreed that they would step over his body and get on with their work. At delivery his wife needed the assistance of forceps, and he just strolled out while the baby was being delivered and was back in the room again immedi-ately he heard the baby's birth cry.

For anyone to be a good support person in labour it is not just a question of saying, 'You're doing very well', or 'Yes, breathe like that, dear!' or 'Won't be long now' – although all these may help. It is rather a matter of sharing an experience; and this not in the sense of collapsing under the weight of a burden, or of being overwhelmingly excited with the drama of all that is going on, but of sensitively participating in the woman's hopes and accomplishment, and also of helping her to *organize* her experience so that it has meaning.

This can be very important when things start slowly, and hour after hour passes with hardly anything happening – a situation most likely to occur with first babies. This very gentle slope leads gradually to dilatation through a long-drawn-out pre-labour phase. There is nothing abnormal about such a state of affairs, but it can be very wearing for the woman in labour.

Then, too, women often lose all sense of time in advanced labour – especially in long labours. This means that they tend to become disoriented, and this in turn leads to a lowering of morale and a feeling of helplessness and hopelessness. 'I'm too tired; I can't go on. Why don't they take it away?' This state of affairs can usually be avoided if she is assisting in keeping her own log book of labour, charting her progress through these stormy seas; and when despair is imminent she can be encouraged to look back and see what progress has been made: 'Contractions were coming every five minutes and lasting 45 seconds. Now they are coming every three minutes and lasting a minute. That's an advance. Soon we shall be going into transition – the bridge between the first and second stages.'

Being with women in labour, and sharing their struggles and triumphs in this way, demands a great outpouring of energy and can be very exhausting. This is why it is really too much to ask as routine of any midwife, however dedicated to her calling and however sympathetic she is as a person. She can give calm guidance and friendship, but cannot involve herself emotionally in every labour, or she would become useless in her task, drained of energy and shattered by the multitude of moving experiences in which she was participating. To really share a labour – like sharing in dying – involves the very depths of one's being. This often happens, in spite of themselves, to those present at birth, and they find their eyes wet with tears as the baby makes its first world-welcoming cry, and the mother reaches out her arms for the child as it swims out of her body.

It is one reason why someone you love is the obvious person to fill this role of labour companion. It is a significant experience in a close relationship, and has an existential reality of its own. A lover is involved completely as a person who has a function which is quite different from that of the purely technical, manipulative, or educational.

The midwife's role is all of these, and labour also involves her as a person, but she is not committed in the same way – is not required to experience it at the same depth, unless, for some reason, this particular labour means something special to her. She is the expert, the professional; she is able to plan, calculate and assess in a way for which the couple are not usually equipped either by training or interest. The couple are wayfarers, explorers in strange territory – and because of this they are together in a different sense, if given the opportunity and support, from the sense in which the midwife and mother are related.

I would not wish to suggest that the midwife's and the

partner's functions are utterly different, because in practice they often overlap, and this harmonious overlapping is part of a good working relationship. Each contributes what they can best offer to the situation. But I do feel that the sexual partner has a role in labour which is not in any way a concession to either sentimentality or obstetric voyeurism, and which does not conflict with that of the doctor or midwife, but which is a much needed supportive and 'sharing' role.

When childbirth is part of a relationship in which the partners are committed to each other, however dramatic and thrilling having a baby is, there is a large part of their lives together which continues, for better or worse, side by side with the pregnancy and the early days and months of parenthood. So merely training a couple for childbirth does not necessarily meet their needs. What they really need to learn is how to adapt themselves to changed roles *vis à vis* each other, and how to enjoy each transitional phase of their lives together. For the whole of a relationship is really a series of transitions, in which the identity of each partner is transmuted by processes involving the birth and development of children, the new stresses involved in changing relationships in the family, and the daily battles and satisfactions and pleasures of living together.

This is why classes that concentrate simply upon teaching about labour and discussing that particular challenge as an act, rather than a developmental experience, fall far short of the sort of help they could be offering. I remember an American obstetrician commenting that he didn't know whether there was really much point in a man helping the woman in labour, since however happy they appeared at the time, he knew of a great many cases in which the couple had separated subsequently, and he quoted the case of two couples who participated in beautiful birth films – and those marriages broke up afterwards. And as he spoke I remembered how helpless and worried one of these men had seemed to me, how the woman's eyes were always on the fatherly obstetrician for guidance and support, how her husband had tried to get her to suck ice because he had been taught to give her ice and how she did not want it and became irritated with him. And the birth itself, with the woman straining and pushing in near desperation – rather than letting her body open up in the great unfolding mystery of sensations as the baby was pressed down the birth canal and fanned open the lips of the vagina and the tissues in and around it – culminating in delivery not apparently out of her body at all, but from a hole in a sheet, draped between other sheets, and over legs suspended in steel lithotomy stirrups and also draped. The whole mystery of sex had been removed from that birth by hospital routines, and by the expert sleight of hand demonstrated by an obstetrician who acted the part almost of a magician as he deftly lifted the baby out. I remember vividly, too, that the mother, still overcome by the intensity of sensations of delivery, and by the struggle in which she had been engaged, was at first reluctant to take and hold her baby, and how she asked the nurse to give the child to her husband – and the nurse refused and insisted that *she* must take it.

In some ways the experts, with the kindliest of intentions, had seemed to me to invade that relationship and to threaten it just where it was most vulnerable. Although the couple had learned techniques of coping with labour, they, and everyone else concerned, had missed the opportunity for increased self-awareness and a deeper understanding of the woman's needs.

However important the woman is in childbirth, and hers must be the central role, the point of having a baby is not simply to provide her with sensations of pleasurable achievement. The couple are doing something together which deeply affects their own partnership, the wider family of which this relationship is a part, and the great network of human relationships extending out into the present and back into time and forward into the future. Childbirth is the focal point of all these relationships; in the act of birth society is changed irrevocably. And when a woman pushes one small, screaming baby out into the world she is in that moment transforming her relationships with her partner, mother and father, other children, sisters and brothers and grandparents, friends, and colleagues at work – and her partner's relationship with all these people, too.

So that is why in this book I have welcomed the chance of recording the experiences of real people, and not only of students of a particular sort of technique of behaviour for childbirth – not simply pupils carrying out a task methodically, but individuals interacting with each other in love and need, and learning a little more about each other as they do so.

Not all labours, of course, are straightforward. And attending classes is not going to ensure that there are no obstetric abnormalities; even when labour is far from 'normal', or when a woman has augmentation of labour with an intravenous drip to stimulate the uterus into greater activity, or has a forceps delivery, vacuum extraction, or Caesarean section, her personal experience of labour is not simply the sum of all these events. Her own personality can, and often does, transmute each isolated event, and the whole physiological process, into something which has value in terms of her thinking and feeling about her own identity, and what human relations and life itself mean to her. Childbirth is then part of a larger system of values, part of a pattern. Every pattern has something satisfying about it when it is contrasted with chaos, whether this is a chaotic sequence of events which we don't understand, the confusion which comes with disorientation of mental processes, or the sort of stress situation in living in which we cannot see what to do, what action we can perform, or what role we can play – like 'shell shocked' soldiers in battle or rats in a maze which have been deliberately frustrated and confused in a laboratory situation.

Even a quick, easy labour can be chaotic in just this sort of way if the woman goes into it unprepared. And a long, difficult labour can provide its own satisfactions if the woman knows what she can do to help, and sees order and meaning instead of muddle and a bombardment of meaningless sensations.

Not all the women in these pages had their babies easily. I have included difficult labours, ones which left the woman feeling frustrated and angry, some births in which the baby had to be rushed straight to intensive care, and two stillbirths. No method of preparation can possibly ensure that labour is going to be straightforward and simple or that every baby is going to be, as some doctors put it, 'a blue ribbon', 'top quality' baby. Some women had long and arduous labours lasting several days. It is important to emphasize this because sometimes when we explain the advantages of education for childbirth the response is, 'Oh, but she would have had an easy labour anyway; she's just the type for it' . . . 'She was in her early twenties, but I'm nearly forty!' . . . 'They say I may need a Caesarean section' . . . 'My husband isn't allowed in the delivery room' . . . 'I've had this bad back ever since I was in my teens' . . . 'My blood pressure is up' or 'I have asthma, so how can I do breathing exercises!' . . . 'I had a threatened miscarriage and the doctor says I must rest' . . . 'I really can't spare the time now because I've got to get my thesis in before the baby is born' . . . 'They don't have anyone at the hospital who can remind me of my breathing so what's the point?' . . . 'There is a history of very difficult births in my family; none of us have babies easily' . . . or even, 'My husband' . . . or, 'My doctor . . . thinks it's better if I don't know too much, because I worry'. Childbirth education helps a woman cope better, whatever kind of labour she has. She may still need a Caesarean section, but she will know what to do and when to do it, is able to understand what is happening and shares in all the decisions made about her body and her baby and she comes out of it feeling much more a person than the woman who is reduced, from the moment she enters hospital, to being just the body on the table. A woman may suffer severe backache in labour but there are special techniques for helping her to handle 'backache labour' so that the baby's weight is taken off the spine as much as possible, and her morale is maintained through the long hours of dilatation. And the women who think they are 'not the type' for childbirth often find that preparation helps them to become more flexible, less anxious and more assertive about what they want. The most unlikely women can learn how to adapt to their labours. I know women who have started off rigid with fear: 'Quite frankly, I'm terrified of the whole thing', who reach the end of the pregnancy saying, 'I can't wait for the birthday; I'm so excited.'

I remember a woman who suffered from extreme mood-swings – from a state of being 'giddy and gay and darting about' and 'always in a whirl', as she said, to its opposite, when she felt life was not worth living. She was single, had been losing blood right through early pregnancy, and smoked nonstop (not good for the baby, as the placenta cannot sieve off the poisonous chemicals in tobacco smoke). No one in her family thought that she would ever have the self-discipline or concentration to practise exercises, or the self-control not to go to pieces in labour. But she managed beautifully. It seemed, in fact, the first thing she had done all by herself, and at which she had been really successful. 'It was *very* interesting,' she told me. 'But it would have been terrible if you didn't know about it. As it was I felt I knew everything that was happening, and the breathing was *marvellous*. I didn't have much pain. In fact, I wandered round most of the first stage – no problems that way at all, and it was all ever so easy to deal with.' It was only afterwards, when she reached the end of her story, that I learned that the baby did not come down the birth canal in the correct position, and that she was delivered by forceps. To the mother this was purely incidental compared to the happiness and sense of achievement she felt about having given birth to her baby.

The women who form the *dramatis personae* of these pages are no paragons. They are not possessed of superhuman powers of endurance, and they vary in the degree to which they perceive and suffer pain, their health, the books they read, the jobs they do, their social class, cultural background, education, and in what they want childbirth to be. Some of them had emotional problems which made them doubt their ability to give birth naturally or to be a good mother, or even to go on living positively, with anything to contribute to life. These had often sought me out because they knew that problems interested me and I was not keen on simply teaching exercises and explaining physiological processes. Often in an accompanying letter from their doctors there were remarks about Mrs S. 'not being able to relax', or being 'tense', 'apprehensive', 'fearful' or 'depressed'. So in a way we were not starting off with the highest of hopes, and we knew it might be a hard, long struggle. Some had not really wanted a baby at all, or at any rate, not then; a few were single and unsupported, and some had contemplated having an abortion and felt guilty, ashamed, or worried about possible effects on the baby. One or two had tried to finish their own lives. Others had had psychiatric treatment and had been in mental hospitals, sometimes for years. Some were trapped in a partnership which was not happy; some had been through a stage of their lives when they were addicted to drugs. And apart from all these difficulties, some women knew that their own mothers had suffered terribly in childbirth, that there was a history of difficult birth in their families, or had endured sexual trauma themselves – rape and incest – which had destroyed their pleasure in sex and in their own bodies. And there was a wide range of physical illnesses, including severe asthma, pelvic injury and, of course, the raised blood pressure, excessive weight gain, oedema of the tissues and albumin in the urine which presents the classic picture of pre-eclampsia. And in age they range from seventeen to forty-two.

This must sound as if we are an odd lot! But if one looks behind the faces in any crowd and sees the lines of worry and the pattern of muscle tensions which betray anxiety, it becomes clear that even the most ordinary looking people can be living in private turmoil, and that none of us are without our problems. It is only that we choose to operate as if we were all fairly stable and contented individuals simply because to do anything else, to give time to listen, or to reach out with sympathetic understanding, would prove too time consuming, exhausting and disturbing. In ordinary situations of living we cannot afford to 'take the lid off'; we agree implicitly on standards of social behaviour which inhibit the expression of our deepest fears or our worst doubts. It seems to me, however, that antenatal counselling provides opportunity for coming face to face with some of these problems, and that this may often be necessary before the woman can go forward happily into her labour or be able to enjoy being a mother. In my own teaching course I see each woman privately, usually with her partner too, if she has one, at least once for a consultation which can last anything from one hour to a whole evening, and we use the group not only for doing exercises and imparting information, but also for discussion of all the emotional and social aspects of childbearing.

Emotions in pregnancy and birth are not inconvenient symptoms which need to be nullified by drugs, or by escape from sensation. The emotional changes of pregnancy can often provide clues as to what needs to be done and the necessary adjustments in interpersonal relationships. As J. A. C. Brown says,*

'Freud devised a means of diagnosing man's troubles, not of suppressing them, and the emotions we are so desirous of suppressing are the mental equivalents of body symptoms which may give warning that all is not well . . . The very real danger today is that neuroses may cease to be dealt with by psychological methods based on understanding at all, and that with new pharmacological and medical or surgical methods we shall be "cured" by being made insensible to conflicts rather than facing up to them and trying to understand what is wrong with our way of life. Instead of realizing that there are circumstances which justify attitudes of guilt, remorse, shame, anxiety, or injustice, we shall treat them as inconvenient "symptoms" to be dispelled by a tranquilliser or thymoleptic drug.'

Some women worry, on being told that they are 'elderly primips' or that they need a 'trial' of labour, and perhaps Caesarean section, that things are going terribly wrong, and even perhaps that there is no point in preparing themselves for labour, as it is all going to be taken out of their hands anyway. Nothing could be further from the truth and there are several accounts of labour from women having their first babies in their late thirties in the pages that follow. If there are special problems, or if a woman falls into a 'high risk' category, there is all the *more* reason why she should learn how she can help herself to maintain good health, correct posture, and a positive emotional attitude during pregnancy, to use available techniques in response to the stimuli of the contracting uterus and the discomforts of 'backache labour', and also learn how to select from whatever is offered by her attendants those things which she decides are of advantage for herself or her baby. Ignorance and noncomprehension will not help her; understanding can. A good obstetrician works much better when he or she can work *with* the mother and not just *on* her.

This is why so many doctors emphasize the importance of

* *Freud and the Post-Freudians* (Penguin, 1969).

the relationship between themselves and their patients. They often call it one of 'trust'; it need not be a blind leaning on the obstetrician's superior wisdom. It should mean the woman's intelligent participation, adopting not the role of a child, but behaving as an adult participating in a vital life process.

I remember being with one of my students when she was having a vacuum extraction. This was necessary because of transverse arrest as the baby descended the birth canal. She was allergic to various drugs, and in order not to spark off an allergic reaction it was decided to use general anaesthesia for the few moments of delivery during which the vacuum extractor would bring the baby right down on to the perineum, rotating the head in the process, and then suck it out from the mother's body. The obstetrician turned to me and remarked that he had never used the vacuum extractor with an unconscious woman before, that it was inconvenient for him, and not half as easy; he always relied on the informed participation of the mother, and worked *with* her to get the baby born. When a contraction came she told him, and she held her breath and pushed the baby deep into the birth canal, releasing her pelvic floor muscles as she did so, while at the same time he drew the baby forward with suction. In this case he did a beautiful delivery – and the mother woke up to a gorgeous baby. But he made it quite clear that his preference for having the mother's active co-operation was nothing to do with the benefits for the mother's psyche, but was simply a matter of making his task much easier.

Those readers who are expecting to be delivered at home can look forward to the comfort of familiar surroundings and the concentrated personal attention of a midwife who will be with them throughout active labour. This can be a tremendous advantage in helping birth to take place as part of the natural process of living, and not as something strange and rather alarming. We are beginning to rediscover some of the benefits of home birth for both mother and baby – and certainly for the father and for any other children.*† In Britain specially equipped personnel are on hand to speed to the woman's home

---

* *The Place of Birth*, ed. Sheila Kitzinger and John A. Davis (O.U.P., 1980).
† *Birth at Home*, Sheila Kitzinger (O.U.P., 1979).

if necessary. These 'Flying Squads', based on large hospitals, are highly efficient, quick, and, in spite of their name, undramatic. They can deal with post-partum haemorrhage – which can occur when the placenta has not separated properly – and deliver a retained placenta, in the bedroom, staying till all is well.

For many women home birth is a viable option and they should consider it seriously. Only on territory which a woman controls herself is she really free to make her own decisions without feeling under pressure from others and from a system of which she is only one tiny part. Only at home is she a woman giving birth, rather than a patient. Only at home is birth part of the ebb and flow of life, rather than a medical act. Though I include in these birth stories many happy and exultant accounts of birth in hospital, the home birth stories are, on the whole, qualitatively different. Not all women will want to have their babies at home, and it is obviously safer for some to choose hospital because they know there are particular risks for themselves or their babies, but the challenge is for us to try and create in hospital an environment which not only *looks* like home but *feels* like home – and that may turn out to be impossible.

Pregnancy and the Couple's Relationship

Most of the women in these pages had a partner with them during childbirth. Birth was not just an isolated incident in their lives together, but part of a continuum which included the whole experience of childbearing, becoming parents and growing as parents.

For a couple the nine months' waiting is in many ways a time of preparation. Not only is the woman's body altering but sutble changes are often taking place in her outlook on life, the way she feels about herself and her body, and frequently even in her interests too. She may have been the last woman ever to peep in a pram as it stood waiting outside a shop, but now everything about babies can become almost enthralling. A man may begin to wonder what has come over the woman he knew, who was interested in the same sort of things as he was. She may be more easily moved to laughter and tears, more quickly upset by each petty quarrel, more snappily critical of her mother, mother-in-law or colleagues at work. She may talk so much about the baby or her exercises that he is bored stiff with the whole business and only wishes it was over with. Or she may be happier and more relaxed and suddenly more sure of herself and confident in the idea of motherhood, as if at last she has a chance of being something and doing something she always wanted to be and do. The man can feel that she no longer needs him in the same way, and that their relationship has changed – and not for the better.

Nights may be far from peaceful because the expectant mother is at her most vulnerable in the hours of darkness, and may be unable to drop off to sleep, or may wake up and worry in the early hours of the morning. Sometimes she has had bad or disturbing dreams, which she may not remember, and they can amount to nightmares. One of these women, for instance, had reported dreams of being strapped to a delivery table with the baby separate from her in a glass bottle. Once the baby is kicking vigorously this alone may be enough to cause disturbed sleep, and if the bed is small neither partner may be getting enough sleep. This is the time to buy a larger bed if funds will run to it, or to push two beds together if the room is large enough, perhaps a double and a single side by side. (They can always visit each other.)

Sessions at the hospital or health centre may be matters of great moment, and she seems to go on endlessly about what 'they' said and what 'they' did to her, and whether Peggy, who is due at the same time, is bigger or about the same size as she is, and whether she is putting on too much weight. Some of the women in these pages commented to me, at one time or another, 'I come back from the clinic and I just burst into tears!' I remember one saying in despair, 'They reduced me to *nothing*.' For a man, this is another world, and he may find it difficult to understand why she should get 'worked up' because the doctor or a nurse said something to her which she interprets as meaning that everything is not going well, the baby is not big enough, or she is not big enough, or her pelvis is too small, or her perineum is tight.

In advanced pregnancy she carries on an extraordinary two-way conversation with the world outside her – other people, things she can see and hear and communicate with in the outside world – and with the baby inside her, moving deep in her body. This can be uncanny for a man and he may find it a disturbing element in their relationship – especially when they make love and he feels this sudden other life. Women themselves interpret these stirrings of life in many different ways too; some finding them pleasurable, even exciting, others hating them and conceptualizing the baby as an invader of their bodies, or as a parasite growing inside.

And ahead of her lies the labour. It is unfashionable today for a woman to admit to fear of childbirth. When I meet women for their private consultations at the start of the childbirth course I find that even the most obviously worried, nervous woman will try to avoid such an admission, as if there were something shameful and disgraceful about it. There is a general attitude that, now that women can learn so much more about their bodies, there is no reason why they should be alarmed, and that to be so is silly and irrational.

Yet childbirth is an utterly new experience and one which,

however commonly it is enacted every minute of every day all over the world, involves almost incredible physiological processes when one actually imagines it happening to one's own body. What is more natural than some misgivings about being launched into the unknown? In any similar situation we should also – and quite reasonably – be apprehensive. Any man, however 'macho', might feel apprehensive when confronted by such an experience, and anxiety of this kind is not a 'feminine characteristic'.

For such anxiety alerts and signals attention. It can be used constructively to initiate a positive course of action, just as someone cooks ahead when expecting a number of weekend guests or as the sailor reefs her sails and presents less canvas to the wind when a gale is approaching. One need not be helplessly at the mercy of events. As Charles Rycroft says, in *Anxiety and Neurosis**, 'The capacity to be anxious is a biological function necessary for survival.' Anxiety can serve the function of mobilizing energy, marshalling forces to meet a challenge.

This may be why a woman who is obviously anxious and who cannot relax during early pregnancy, may actually cope quite well in labour, and surprise both herself and her attendants.

So some anxiety is a normal occurrence in pregnancy, but the subjects on which it is focused vary, and it is wrong to suppose that all anxiety associated with childbearing is linked with fear of pain in labour. Even if the woman *says* that is what worries her (and this is the sort of thing which seems a satisfying answer in a questionnaire for instance), she often does so in an interview only because she feels she has been driven into a corner and has to say *something*.

This sort of problem can probably never be understood by tackling it as if anxiety could be put into clearly defined categories of 'fear of pain', 'that something will happen to the baby', or of death. Because women sometimes deceive even themselves over what they are distressed about, let us examine more closely the vague feelings of threat – often very diffuse –

* Penguin, 1970.

which are frequently associated with this venture into the unknown.

There is often, of course, fear of pain which is more than she is able to bear. But the vital element in this may be the dread that she will break down, 'make a fool of herself', cry out or swear, fling off her clothes, or say irrational things, and that thus an uglier but truer self will be revealed. To do this is to put herself in a shameful situation – one which she feels she deserves. It is met by social scorn and ridicule. It is this humiliating aspect of how a woman sees childbirth that forms the kernel of the anxiety. Physically exposed, emotionally exposed, subjugated by the act of birth, and under the critical eye of midwives and doctors (or this is how she sees it) she will be humiliated by her own self-revelation and by a train of actions over which she has no control.

The woman who feels like this does not only suffer from a dread of exposure in labour. This is part of a much larger and more general fear that her defences will collapse. It is useless for a woman to face up to this problem as if it existed solely in the context of childbirth. It may be very important for her, and an opportunity for increased self-awareness and maturation when she can say to herself, 'Yes, I feel I have to keep all the barriers up tight because I might so easily overstep the mark. I have all this nastiness and ugliness inside me and I'm afraid of it bursting out.' It is then that education for childbirth can help her to see that being a woman, having a baby, and experiencing the sweep of emotions she has then and in the love relationship of which the conception and birth is an integral part, is fascinating and beautiful. The preparation for birth is touching on the wider sphere of her whole psychological life, and not only on the fact of pushing a baby out into the world.

Another vortex of anxiety centres round a fear of disintegration – the very loss of the self. This may also be connected with feeling that childbirth is a humiliating process, but there is an additional element – that she must not lose control, take any form of drug or accept any assistance from medical or nursing staff lest her personality dissolve. This sounds fairly improbable – even amusing – on paper, but in fact it is a terrifying notion. Ibsen, in *Peer Gynt*, wrote about the man who was nothing, and when onion skin after onion skin was peeled away to try to find the essential man underneath, there was nothing there.

The anxious woman may fight all along the way, rigid and resisting, bound by muscle tensions with which she seeks unconsciously to define and frame her body, her physical identity, and trace the boundaries of her body image.

For each of us the ego grows out of our gradually increasing physical awareness as babies – the sensory groping to know the world around. Each reaching out movement, whether of tongue, lips and gums, or of eye, or hand or hearing, results in a defining of self and its limits, as well as knowledge of the surrounding environment. At first the new baby cannot know where the self leaves off and the mother begins. But bit by bit the concept of self and otherness is built up, and this is based on and expressed through the body. Yet the body we visualize ourselves as having may be rather different from the body that other people see, especially in times of rapid change, as in pregnancy. Pregnancy and birth, like puberty, the menopause, old age, and dying, involve physical metamorphosis, a period of transition between one state of physiological being and another. They all form transitional crises, bridges also between different concepts of the self and different roles in society.

If a woman has never experienced a sense of *completeness* and firmly established identity – of being herself and content *in* herself – pregnancy may prove an acute threat to her self-image in just this way. The satisfying defined boundaries of the self are difficult to achieve unless the individual has had some experience of success – of having achieved something (whether it is school work, or pottery, or horse-riding, or dancing, cookery, or simply being a person in her own right), and this is gradually constructed during childhood in person-to-person relationships with those we love or esteem. (To lack this is to suffer denial of one of the basic rights of a child who reaches out to attempt to master the universe.) Everyone needs this experience of success, initially in the eyes of loved parents. When a woman has never felt secure in this she embarks on the challenge of childbearing feeling that she is bound to fail and 'let people down', and under great stress she may feel that her identity will disappear like a drop of water evaporating in the air. This sense of threatened identity is increased when she is subjected to procedures and interventions in childbirth over which she has no control. It is an experience which at times in our lives we probably all share. In pregnancy a woman is emotionally fluid and capable of enormous change, and there is not only the challenge of childbirth but also, because of this flexibility, the opportunity of increased self-awareness.

The pregnant woman may be part of a loving relationship with another person who can help this process by in some ways taking the place of the parents. For in many ways we seek from our partners the things we wanted from our parents – some of which we may have been denied. Often a woman recreates her idea of a loving father in the man she loves – not perhaps anything like the man who was actually her father. Or she may have determined to pick a different sort of man and has deliberately chosen one who was in every way the opposite of her idea of her father, and her expectations of his behaviour will be determined by her conceptualization of this rejected image of manhood. It is rather like a stencil from which one can do a tracing either on the inside or the outside of the figure.

A partner may be caught up in this drama of character delineation without knowing why or what is happening. They are not just a 'couple' in isolation, but part of a family, whether they like it or not. That family extends back in time through the generations, frequently repeating its plots and its problems, but in different settings, as well as stretching its branches out in the present and future.

All this can come to a head during a pregnancy in which the woman is suffering from anxiety. So often the problems are explained away as being due to her 'unstable emotional state': 'She is a bit weepy,' they say, 'because she's expecting the baby'; 'Don't take any notice. Take her out and she'll forget about it'; so evading the issue, and the opportunity. It is then too that fear of childbirth may be produced as the excuse for the upset. But this is not the point, for the crisis of giving birth is the occasion and symbol for many things which really describe a state of personal identity in relation to others.

One of the signs that a woman needs more help than she is getting is if she is not sleeping well – either failure to get to sleep or waking in the night. We have seen that this may be because the baby is so active, or may be because she has to keep on emptying her bladder, or has indigestion or heartburn. Not being able to sleep is often explained by reference to these physiological causes. But I have noticed that when a woman has the opportunity to talk she often begins to remember disturbing dreams, and worries that have occupied her mind at two or three in the morning when she lay awake in the darkness. In quiet and unhurried discussion she is then often able to face up to some of her fears. But to do this somebody must be prepared to listen without judgement, or slick interpretation, or trying to sweep problems away as if they did not matter with a 'Don't worry, everything will be all right', and simply offer friendship and understanding companionship. This is where a partner who can give time to listen can help most constructively, and where the childbirth educator who provides more than training classes can also help.

Sometimes women just cannot express in words what they feel. Occasionally they can help themselves best by painting, drawing or modelling clay – somehow giving their fears objective reality, bringing them outside themselves. The woman who had the terrifying dreams about delivery did this, and produced a vivid and disturbing painting. I often use her paintings when we talk in class about fear of pregnancy, and I told her how helpful they were. 'It helped me to do the paintings,' she said, 'but what helps me most of all is the thought that they are of some use, and that what I went through isn't just wasted.' The creation of an acceptable channel for the expression of emotion is a logical method of handling stress, and very much better than bottling it all up and pretending that everything is all right if it is not.

The emotions which are often worked through can put extra stress on a relationship, so that it looks as if the baby, far from cementing the partnership, could actually destroy it. The child can then become the scapegoat. But it really starts when the couple can no longer find a basis for shared experience. From then on the nappies hanging to dry, the baby's demands, his preoccupation with what is going on in the office, his remarks about her mother and her friends, and hers about his friends, his untidiness or insensitivity, the way he behaves with other women, even the television programme each wants to watch, can produce sparks to feed the flames of resentment, jealousy, and even hate. Childbirth can be a peak experience in a woman's life, one full of challenge and excitement, deep satisfaction and joy, which she recollects with delight many years afterwards. The birth of a baby can also be a growing-point in a relationship. For most couples who wrote these birth stories the births of their babies were a shared experience – not an isolated one, not an end in itself, not just a 'beautiful happening' – but part of a growing relationship in which each became more vividly aware of the other's needs and the other's reality and they felt afterwards that they understood each other better.

PART TWO

The Births

Hardly a day goes by without my receiving a woman's account of her labour. Some of these accounts are from women who have attended my own childbirth classes or who have sought my help during pregnancy in order to get the kind of birth experience they want, or to cope with emotional difficulties. Many others have come in connection with five research projects on which I have been engaged – women's experiences of induction of labour, antenatal care, episiotomy, epidurals and the making of birth plans. I have always believed that if I asked women to help with my research there is a commitment on my part to continue being interested in what happens afterwards – something which I gladly accept – and in being readily available to listen and share in women's experiences.

Other accounts again arrive from readers of my books in many different countries. These often finish with a sentence apologizing for 'bothering' me or for being 'boring' or 'long-winded'. No apology has ever been necessary. I am always fascinated by women's birth stories, especially if they reveal what the experience meant to them psychologically and in terms of their self-identity, rather than merely being a record of events. From every single woman I have learned something which has helped me understand better what birth is all about. I am enormously grateful to all those women who have told me of their first-hand experiences.

It is on some of these accounts from different sources that this section of the present book is based. I have edited them only if they were very long or if the meaning was not clear, because I wanted women to speak for themselves. I have also included accounts by fathers who were sensitive and emotionally aware of what was happening, and a couple by children who were present at birth.

For those readers who are not familiar with the sequence of events in childbirth, it may help to have a brief introduction to the usual pattern of labour.

Before labour really starts, the cervix – or the neck of the uterus – which hangs down in the vagina like the neck of a bottle, becomes soft and 'ripe'. Pre-labour contractions – tightenings of the uterus – may start to open the cervix – dilate it – by a few centimetres. These contractions last about half a minute and may be irregular or some ten to twenty minutes apart. They may be uncomfortable, but are usually painless. This process can take a week or more.

When labour starts, contractions become more frequent, often about five to seven minutes apart, and each one lasts longer – maybe a minute. When the uterus contracts, longitudinal muscles running from top to bottom of what is virtually a bag of muscle in which the baby nestles, are pulled up, shortened and thickened. This has the effect of progressively opening circular fibres around the cervix.

The *first stage* is the part of labour during which the cervix is opening up like this. Towards the end of this stage of dilatation, when the cervix is almost fully dilated, like a tight polo-neck sweater through which the crown of the baby's head is being firmly pressed, the stretching of muscle fibres and other tissues and the pressure produced by contractions is usually painful. Contractions are most difficult to handle then, and may last between a minute and a minute and a half.

The final part of the first stage is *transition*. This is the phase between 7 cm and full dilatation of the cervix when contractions are coming one on top of another, more or less unpredictably, and sometimes with two peaks. A lip of the cervix is still holding in the baby's head. The urge to start pushing the baby out may come at first during this phase, accompanied by rectal pressure and an involuntary catch in the breath. It is best to avoid active pushing until the cervix is fully dilated so that the tissues around the cervix have time to open up further without stress being put on them.

When the cervix is completely dilated it forms a circular opening about the size of a large hand including the thumb joint. There is often a lull at this point and contractions die down or become spaced further apart. This tends to happen when the baby's head is still high. It is a good time to get refreshed and rested, ready for the onset of the second stage.

The woman knows when the *second stage* – usually much

shorter than the first stage – starts because she cannot avoid pushing, and often wants to do so very urgently and passionately. When she does so, it is important that she opens up below. As the baby's head descends on to the perineum, the tissues between and around the anus and vagina gradually fan out with the steady pressure from above downwards, and the top of the baby's head can be seen in the vagina. At the height of each push it appears and then seems to recede between contractions as the lips of the vagina close over it again.

Delivery is preceded by the *crowning* of the baby's head. It comes to the opening and does not slip back again between contractions. From this point on the mother breathes out the baby unless instructed to do otherwise. She does not push deliberately but lets the uterus do its expulsive work alone. The baby slides out, first the head, followed by the shoulders and then the rest of the body.

After the birth the uterus goes on contracting. During the *third stage* the placenta, or after-birth, becomes peeled off the lining of the uterus and slips into the vagina. The mother feels the contraction and gives a push – or several pushes – until the placenta is delivered. Then, if all has gone well, in one mother's words, 'It is all over bar the cheering! Wonderful feeling. Thanks everyone! Thanks world!'

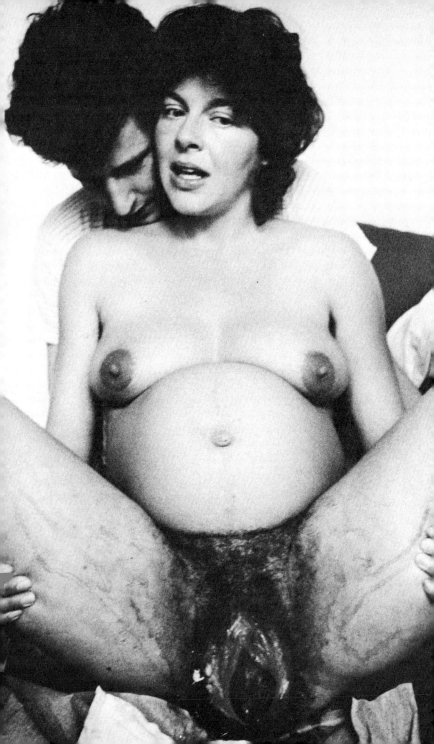

An Easy Birth

Even in a straightforward, easy labour a woman may experience a torrent of conflicting emotions – excitement, doubt, hope, fear, anxiety, joy, anger, weariness, irritation, disbelief, and utter satisfaction and peace. Here a woman describes her emotions during the birth of her first child.

Labour began early in the morning with slight bleeding, a week before the estimated date of delivery. I didn't believe it was 'the real thing' at first, I didn't want to be disappointed if it wasn't. I began to think that I must prepare things to take to hospital 'just in case' and worrying that I wouldn't be ready in time. As the day progressed I had some pains, but infrequently. They were quite bearable and I got on with things around the house, still not at all sure that labour had started. I felt restless, and also didn't want to leave the house. I was expecting the early stage to be more painful and less gradual.

It was only in the early evening that the contractions became more frequent and sharp. I kept on feeling that I wanted to go to the toilet. Peter started to time the contractions, but they didn't seem to be at all regular. I was still telling myself that it must be only a preparation for labour. I was moving around the house, cooking supper, and again I thought that this wouldn't be the case if it was really labour. We then rang the hospital as the contractions got more intense. I was very nervous of going there too soon and when the midwife said we should go in for a check to see what was happening I felt worried that I was just panicking and it was all too soon. I had a bath, thinking that this would help things along, and soon after this the mucus plug broke. Then I fully believed that I was really in labour.

When I left to go to the hospital I felt reluctant to leave the security of our home. I saw people in the streets going about doing ordinary things, waiting for buses, whatever, and here I was in labour, driving off to the hospital to have a baby, a world apart from them.

Once we arrived at the hospital everything happened in a

Mouth soft and relaxed, the mother breathes out her baby's head.   57 timeless bubble. I still felt this might not really be labour and that contractions would stop. I was examined by the midwife, who I met for the first time. She was quiet and calm and careful, letting me stop her if I felt a contraction coming. I really couldn't believe I was 6 cm dilated already. Peter and I felt delighted with this. Our midwife showed us to a room, having asked what kind of bed we preferred. I chose the Borning bed.* She then made it clear that the room was ours. Each time she entered she would knock, and we both felt this was a very nice gesture. We had just a side light, so the room looked less austere, but it could have been made more homely.

Everything then seemed to speed up, the waters broke with a great gush and contractions were faster and much stronger. There was no turning back, I felt taken over by great surges in my body. There was no time to think about anything else. I squatted on the bed, I didn't want to move, there was so much movement in my body. I leant over a bean-bag, trying to breathe my way through each wave. I had no sense of time and for the most part I lost sight of Peter and the midwife. At times I would come out of this state and be aware of Peter by my side trying to help me with breathing or holding me. I used the gas and oxygen, but I wasn't sure how much it helped. I felt pulled apart from head to toe. I thought all my insides would come out. I felt I would be sick. I didn't feel afraid, but I did wonder how much more I could take. I was worried it would just get stronger and stronger and not stop. Trying not to push seemed impossible. I became very self-centred and forgot the baby was having to go through something too. I shocked myself when I realized I felt anger towards the baby. How could he do this to me? But this soon passed.

Then everything changed. Having been pulled, trying to resist pushing, I now felt much quieter. I didn't want to do anything but be still for a while. I wasn't exhausted, I still had plenty of energy, but it seemed right that there should be a lull in the process, not a continuous crescendo. But it was at this point my midwife began to encourage me to push, and she and a colleague who arrived expressed an urgency to get it all over.

* A special delivery chair in which the mother can be upright.

They couldn't understand why I seemed to hold back from pushing. I couldn't explain this or resist their pressure. Both Peter and I got swept along in their sense of urgency. Then my body began to move of it's own accord. I couldn't have stopped myself from bearing down, but I felt it shouldn't have been so rushed. Also there was much attention paid to listening to the baby's heart-beat on the fetal monitor, which was held to my tummy, and I felt anxious, thinking there was something wrong – although there wasn't – and felt guilty that I wasn't pushing hard enough. I changed from sitting up on the bed into a kneeling position and this was much better. I found the second stage less painful than the end of the first stage, and I instinctively feel it would have been even easier had I taken a short break to gather myself before the final stage.

When our baby was born I felt certain he was all right. I saw him between my legs and all I could think was how big he was. I couldn't quite believe, despite going through labour, that he had been inside me. I was overwhelmed. He was laid on my breast and I felt incredibly calm and at peace. I then noticed all the blood and shit on the bed and was surprised that I hadn't been aware of this before. I had been worried I would be inhibited about making a mess and in fact none of this had mattered. I then saw the time and realized that two and a half hours had passed since we arrived at the hospital. It could have been a matter of minutes, or hours and hours. I had no sense of time. Once the umbilical cord stopped pulsating, Peter cut it. He had been the one to see if we had a boy or a girl and to check all his toes and fingers. I hadn't even thought to do this! Our baby boy began to root around and then to suckle.

The placenta didn't separate and after an hour the midwife said I should have an injection. She did let me try to push it out without needing this, but I was bleeding and so she said an injection would be best. Once my baby was born and all was well, the third stage seemed an anti-climax. I had to have some stitches. All I really wanted was for the three of us, Peter, our baby and me, to be left alone together. Our baby was weighed and measured and Peter was rather upset by these things being done to him. When we were finally on our own we put on a tape of Vivaldi. This helped to make the room feel much more our space. Peter was restless. I felt peacefully tired. He wasn't helped by the fact there was nowhere comfortable for him to sit. This is where being in our own home would have been so much nicer. We realized it was dawn. I couldn't say much, I felt so overwhelmed. After some time we went to the ward and I took our son to bed with me. I felt he needed to stay with me after spending nine months never parted from me. Peter left and I heard the car drive away. Then I wept tears of joy.

It took me several days at least before I began to feel a sense of familiarity with our baby, getting to know him. It was easier once we left hospital. He then felt much more mine. The first night home we all went to bed, our baby in a cradle beside us. After I had put the light out we heard a snuffling sound. Peter and I simultaneously asked what the noise was, then we both realized there was someone else in the room: our baby!

A Family Birth

Birth is a family matter and it matters to the family. Older children often ask to be there when a baby is born and look forward to it eagerly. They want to be able to help and to share in the excitement. Some women choose not to have an older sibling there because they feel he or she may be restless and will affect their concentration. Or they are worried about the child's reaction to seeing them in pain and witnessing blood. Many find that hospitals are not open to the idea of other children being present at birth and are rather shocked when it is suggested. Some women assume that a child is better out of it because they have never considered the alternative.

Here a woman describes a labour in which her two older boys, aged seven and almost four, actively helped, and the older boy tells the story from his point of view.

Our beautiful baby daughter, Jenny, was born at home with her daddy and big brothers in attendance; also the midwife, of course, and a good friend of ours, Stephanie, who came to look after the boys.

Very early on in the pregnancy, we told our two sons, then seven and nearly four, that we were going to have another baby. We thought it a good idea to give them lots of time to get used to it. One night, after their bedtime story, we talked a little about our coming baby. They were wondering what would happen to them on the day the baby came. I had already arranged a home birth and was about five months pregnant by this time. Quite spontaneously they then asked if they could be there at the birth. I was taken aback slightly because it was a new idea to me, but I promised to discuss it with daddy.

His immediate reaction was, 'Yes, what a good idea.' We discussed it in detail and decided to let them be as much involved as possible, so from then on we looked at lots of books, watched any helpful TV programmes, and did lots of talking about how babies are born, without romanticizing the subject.

Later I plucked up courage to tackle the midwife. Much to my surprise she was in favour so long as everything went well

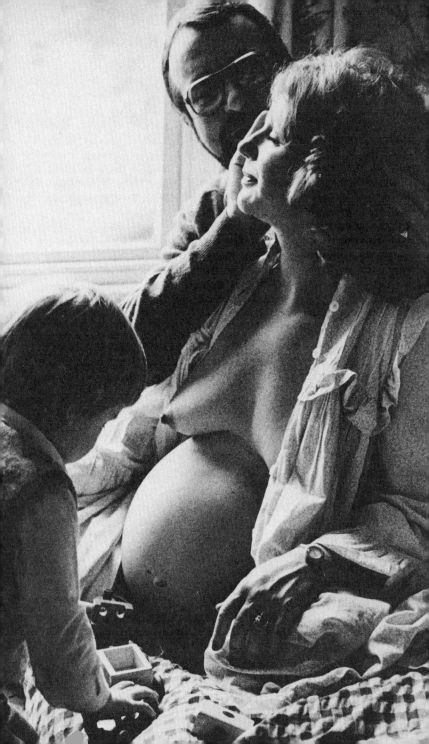

and we had someone here to look after the boys. So we lined up Stephanie to help out.

I did not have any problems at all arranging a home delivery. My GP was delighted to be asked. I am the only patient who has asked him to do one in the last ten years. He was excellent in his antenatal care, making no fuss about anything, but all the same being very thorough.

The midwife who had cared for me during my pregnancy was off duty when I went into labour, so it was a midwife whom we had never met before who came. This did not cause any problems since she was very supportive and had the courage to wait for the birth to happen.

My GP came to see me during labour but missed the delivery. He then arrived soon after and made a very careful job of suturing my small tear. He visited every day for over a week, even though both Jenny and I were fine and had no problems at that stage.

The boys were wonderful; they ran errands, rubbed my back while James, my husband, was supporting me during contractions, took phone calls, and finally they were just sitting there. I made rather a lot of noise in the second stage but it only lasted one minute so it was soon over and they were thrilled and awed to have a new sister.

Jenny was put to the breast immediately after birth. What an intense pleasure it was for me to be cuddling another new baby, and a daughter, when I had convinced myself we would have another boy! We did not really mind, but having a daughter after two sons is an added bonus.

Anyway, try as I might to encourage her to suck, or even just lick, she simply would not and was quite content to be snuggled up close and warm. The midwife had agreed not to give me the routine shot of syntometrine [a uterine stimulant], so we waited and waited for the placenta to be expelled, but nothing happened. However, my blood loss was officially 'less than minimal' so we had no worries about it. After almost an hour we decided that we had waited long enough. I had the shot of syntometrine and the placenta shot out.

The boys were fascinated by the afterbirth and asked to look at it. They will not need to ask where babies come from! Jenny began to nurse vigorously. She obviously just needed to think about it first. Since then she has been a very keen nurser.

Now, at eight months, Jenny shows no interest in solids and is a very happy, healthy and contented, totally breast-fed, baby. People often remark on her ready smile. I attribute this to meeting her needs by always keeping her close and by nursing her whenever she asks. As long as she is in my arms or in the baby carrier we can go anywhere and she will be quite unperturbed. Jenny has brought extreme pleasure to the whole family and is surrounded by her own little circle of love.

There has been no hint of jealousy from either of the boys. They both love their baby sister very much and cannot do enough for her. Now she rewards them with her delightful responses it is beautiful to see.

When my Sister was Born

It was Tuesday the first of March and my mummy said she was ready to pop. First we phoned Stephanie, our friend, who was coming to look after us. Then my mummy phoned the midwife. My little brother and Stephanie were playing with our Scalextric when the midwife arrived.

Mummy was in the bath. The midwife took my mummy in her bedroom for an examination. My little brother had oxtail soup for his lunch. My mummy kept having contractions. I held mummy's hand. I was a bit apprehensive because even though I had been told what would happen by my mummy I knew anything could go wrong.

We waited a while and mummy's contractions kept getting closer and closer together. And with a lot of pushing (from all of us) out popped a head, some shoulders, a body, and a pair of legs. Stephanie said: 'Oh look, it's a girl.' I put a poster in our bay window saying:

'IT'S A GIRL'

For tea we had steak and chips. I really enjoyed it (the tea, I mean).

'I wanted to savour every moment'

One reason why some women decide on home birth is because a previous hospital birth has been sheer torture. They believe that interference in the physiological process made labour unnecessarily painful and difficult and introduced dangers to which they and their babies would not have been exposed if they had been allowed to labour in peace and undisturbed. They think it would not only be more comfortable, but actually safer, to have the next baby at home.

In this account a woman who had what she calls 'a horrific' labour, culminating in a forceps delivery, with her second baby in a high-tech hospital, makes the brave decision to have a home birth next time. It turns out to be 'a dream come true'. She starts by recalling the previous labour and its aftermath.

Last time I was booked into the GP unit, but because I was six days over my EDD [estimated date of delivery] my doctor transferred me to the consultant unit. There I was subjected to every form of interference available, against my wishes. Eventually I begged for a general anaesthetic and a forceps delivery was carried out. Twelve agonizing hours strapped flat on to a bed was physical and mental torture and I knew childbirth was *never* meant to be like this.

The episiotomy took seven months to heal and caused me excruciating pain. I could not sit down, I had to eat my meals standing up, breastfeed my baby lying down on my side and sleep on my tummy. I had a swelling the size of an egg and to pass a bowel movement was a dreadful ordeal. On one occasion I had to think of an excuse for some friends to leave our house as I wanted to use the toilet and couldn't do so without crying with pain. I also had a terrible pain in my right leg, for which I had to take painkillers. Normally I never take any tablets whatsoever, but this was something I couldn't handle.

While we were planning our next baby I asked the consultants (two of them) could I be admitted to the GP unit again for my next baby? They both refused – one offered a trial of labour at 38 weeks after an induction, or a Caesarean at 40 weeks, the other only a Caesarean. I was horrified at their responses and thought a Caesarean was far too drastic – if not downright ridiculous.

At this point I wrote to Sheila for help and to The Society to Support Home Confinements. My husband and I carried out lots of research and with much encouraging advice and support we decided to have our third baby at home.

When I got pregnant I fortunately had no opposition to my request for a home birth. My doctor was a little anxious but I made it clear that I was taking full responsibility and would not tolerate any harassment from anyone.

After a very healthy and happy pregnancy I gave birth at home peacefully and safely to a lovely boy. Even now, five months later, I still feel dizzy wth exhilaration. It was a lovely experience, so basic, yet so vitally important to fulfil. I enjoyed a very quick, exciting three-hour labour (my two previous labours in hospital exceeded 24 hours). I had no drugs whatsoever. The thought of having painkillers never crossed my mind. I was so happy and relaxed at home, I welcomed each contraction, I wanted to savour every moment! During contractions my husband rubbed my back and I rubbed the front of my thighs at the same time. Honestly, this was sufficient to enable me to handle them and I was so thrilled to be told I was already 7 cm dilated when the midwife arrived.

She was sensitive, cheerful and supportive, respected all my wishes and just sat quietly out of sight and allowed my husband and myself to 'get on with it'. She was very happy to deliver my baby in a squatting position on the floor. At 5.45 am she examined me and reported I was 10 cm dilated so we all took up our positions on the floor. My husband sat at the foot of the bed, so I could rest in between his legs during contractions. At 6 am, after only a few pushes, my baby was born and breastfed immediately. What a moment to treasure! To feel a warm, slippery, wide-eyed baby next to one's skin, whose senses are alert as one's own, is really what it's all about. I was amazed at how spontaneous and *gentle* the birth had been. My other two children woke up and saw their new brother with cord intact and everyone was overjoyed.

The placenta was delivered ten minutes later with syntometrine; I just squatted again for the next few contractions. It really was a perfect birth, better than I ever expected. It meant a great deal to me to deliver my baby myself without drugs and interference. I felt in control the whole time. I firmly believe its success was due to the fact that my body was *free* to do its job properly as nature intended and I just relaxed and enjoyed every moment.

I feel privileged to have experienced such a joyful birth at home without drugs. My baby weighed 8 lb 12 oz and even though I am only 4'11" and have 34" size hips I had no trouble pushing him out. There were no eye-bulging, frantic, desperate attempts to push, I knew he would be born soon. I'm convinced squatting or kneeling facilitates the baby's passage into this world. I did tear a little bit and had a few stitches but they caused me no discomfort whatsoever. The midwife did the stitches while I just chewed a wet facecloth.

I hope the choice of a home birth will always be available and I wish it was offered to all parents. I shudder when I think I could have been robbed of this truly marvellous experience and suffered an unnecessary elective Caesarean at the hands of a knife-happy consultant.

A Long, Difficult Labour at Home

Not all home births are easy. A woman needs to prepare herself to handle pain constructively and, if labour turns out to be long, to cope emotionally with the weariness and self-doubts that come as hour follows hour without obvious signs of progress.

This is the story of a slowly unfolding labour during which the woman found that nothing she had learned in childbirth classes really helped her. She tells how, with strong emotional support and comfort from loving helpers, she was enabled to cope well, and in spite of all her negative feelings she hopes to do it all again.

Thomas James was born at 2.43 am on Sunday at home, despite this being my first pregnancy. He weighed 7 lb 7 oz. Labour lasted for 27¼ hours.

I was first aware of contractions when James and I were making love on Friday evening. There was a dull ache low down in my abdomen, rather like a period pain, which passed off fairly soon but recurred about five minutes later. When I realized that this was what contractions were going to feel like I began jotting down how often they were occurring and for how long they were lasting. The first one noted was at 11.30 pm and lasted for about 30 seconds, the second lasted about the same length of time and was eight minutes later.

I felt excited that labour might at last be underway and was awake all night, eagerly anticipating what was going to happen and noting the time and length of contractions. Some second sense earlier in the evening had caused me to unwrap the first set of baby clothes and to put them in the airing cupboard, and for some inexplicable reason I had put make-up on, too – I don't usually like wearing it! Contractions were very mild, and came roughly every five minutes, lasting between 30 and 45 seconds, till about 6.00 am when they became a good deal stronger. Fairly soon after this I had a desperate urge to move my bowels, with pressure so great that I began to panic in case the second stage was about to begin. Eventually, James managed to get through to the doctor who arrived at 7.30 am despite being off

duty. Dr White did a vaginal examination and – to my amaze-
ment and utter disbelief – found me only 1 cm dilated! I began
to feel afraid of what contractions at the end of the first stage
were going to be like, when they already felt so powerful
compared with eight hours earlier. Dr White then left to call in
on Bridget, the midwife, and get her out to us. He promised to
return later.

At 10 am he returned and found me 2 cm dilated, with the
membranes still intact. Throughout the day he and Bridget kept
calling in to keep an eye on things and check on progress.
Things moved very slowly, despite the fact that I had got up
soon after 9.00 am and tried to keep upright and active in the
hope that this would speed things along a bit. Dr White,
however, felt able to go off and play in his rugby match in the
afternoon, so convinced was he that I would not reach the
second stage before the early evening!

By 3.15 pm I had managed to reach 3 cm dilatation, but the
cervix was thinning – at this stage it was 75 per cent effaced
apparently. I was feeling quite despondent at seeing not to
get anywhere after so many hours in labour. It helped a lot to
learn that at least *something* was happening when I was having
a contraction!

Towards the end of the afternoon contractions began to get
even stronger so James and I tried counting backwards from
100 in threes, instead of simply breathing through them. I found
this technique really helpful because I *enjoyed* doing it and it felt
so much more constructive than just concentrating on the
breathing. To be honest, I did not find the breathing nearly as
useful as I had expected, chiefly because it felt too uncomfortable to use the deeper levels of breathing at all, except very early
on in labour, and yet without it I could not give shape to the
contractions. I found that I had a real aversion to 'greeting each
contraction with my breathing' – it seemed so contrived a thing
to do and instead I found myself wanting to say quietly and
calmly that another contraction was just beginning before starting the shallow-chest breathing. It *did* feel right to give a long
breath out at the end of each contraction, however, as an
expression of sheer relief that the pain was at an end for a
while! I suppose the most useful thing about the breathing was

that it kept me from panicking, and prevented me hyperventi-
lating because it kept things rhythmical.

At 6.30 pm Dr White returned – in yellow T-shirt and jeans,
which made everything very much friendlier and less formal –
and soon found that I was only 4 cm dilated. He wanted to
rupture the membranes, and because I was keen for things to
move a little more quickly, as well as begining to feel distinctly
weary of contractions, I agreed to let him do this. It was
painless, but took several attempts before it was successful. I
loved the warmth of the waters as they flowed out, but the
fetus definitely did *not* like being disturbed like this – he moved
more vigorously in the womb than I had ever known in the
whole of the pregnancy. I was very frightened of the effect that
the ARM [artificial rupture of the membranes] might have on
contractions, but to begin with there was little difference in their
intensity, although they did start coming more frequently and
lasting longer. After half an hour, however, they became so
much stronger that I didn't feel able to stay up any longer and
before long they were so powerful that I decided to try the gas
and oxygen. For the next two contractions it seemed to help,
but it didn't make any difference to the third contraction, and I
was sick after that, so I stopped using it then.

At 8 pm Bridget (who remained with us from the rupturing
of the membranes onwards) did another vaginal examination
and found the cervix effaced and closely applied to the baby's
head. I was 4 to 5 cm dilated at this stage and found the
contractions really strong. I don't know whether it was because
of their intensity, or my exhaustion, or the Entonox, but I
began to feel very distant from what was going on. I listened
to my own voice as if it belonged to some third person, and
sounded distinctly drunk! I kept needing to be reminded to
concentrate on my breathing during contractions – I was
instead moaning a lot and protesting vehemently at the pain! I
felt as though I were losing control, and kept thinking that I
was doing very badly. Neither James nor Bridget could convince me otherwise! James had an almost impossible task in
trying to get me to open my eyes and look at him, and to
breathe with him. I didn't want my back rubbed or my
abdomen stroked gently; I didn't want a hot water bottle or an

ice pack; I wouldn't suck chips of ice, though I did suck water from a natural sponge on one occasion – purely to justify having bought it! Every now and then I would have a sip of water, and I found it very soothing to have my forehead wiped with a cool flannel, but what I most wanted was simply to know that James was *there* and to be able to grip his hand tightly during contractions. I couldn't bear the mattress moving at all, while I was having a contraction. It wasn't till Bridget Cheryl pointed out that James had nowhere else to sit and had been cramped up in a tiny corner of the floor for some time that I would let him sit on the bed without becoming very irritated. I felt really ashamed of the way I was behaving, and particularly of the way I was treating James – it wasn't at all how I had intended to cope with labour!

At 10.30 pm, despite many protestations from me, Bridget did another vaginal examination, and to my intense disappointment after all the agony I had been through found that I was no further dilated than I had been at 8 pm. I felt really despondent and was sorely tempted to accept Bridget's offer of pethidine, despite my absolute determination beforehand to have no drugs at all. It was only the knowledge that Dr White was returning in an hour to examine me, and Bridget's honesty in telling me that pethidine would not take the pain away but simply distance me from it and enable me to relax more during contractions, that prevented my taking it; plus remembering a labour report read at our last NCT [National Childbirth Trust] class in which a woman whose labour progressed very slowly to 5 cm took only an hour to go from there to the start of the second stage. I really didn't want to take drugs anyway! I am very relieved that I didn't have it because when Dr White arrived at 11.45 pm I was fully dilated, apart from an anterior lip!

Intensely powerful contractions came one on top of each other, with no break in between, and with one seeming to start even before the previous one had died away. All this did nothing to shift the anterior lip. Dr White tried to push it out of the way with his fingers, but did not succeed, and I got almost to the point of despair. Never have I known two hours pass more slowly! At some point the lip must have gone, but I was not aware of having been told that it had. Bridget said that I could push when I felt I *had* to. At 1.45 am the baby's head was visible, but I didn't take in the fact that crowning had occurred.

Before long Bridget said that if she did an episiotomy I would have my baby with the next contraction. I was feeling so exhausted by then that I felt it would be worth all the subsequent discomfort, and agreed to let her do it, even though I had previously been determined to avoid an episiotomy if at all possible. It wasn't simply for my convenience that Bridget suggested episiotomy, she felt that the tissues would tear if she didn't do it, although previously she had thought I might manage without. Anyway, after it had been done, there, all of a sudden, was Thomas's head between my legs. He had an incredible expression on his face – of tremendous nobility and wisdom – and was absolutely silent. Bridget told me to push with the next contraction. I couldn't wait for that, so keen was I to have my baby in my arms, so I just pushed straight away and before I knew what was happening Bridget put his wriggling, moist, red body on to my stomach. It was the most fantastic moment I have ever known; I loved the feel of his naked, wet body against mine, and the anger with which he uttered his lusty cries. He seemed so huge, and so full of life, with all his limbs writhing strongly in protest at being born.

I was aware of a complete transformation in me; I felt so tender and calm and loving, once I had contact with Thomas, instead of angry and aggressive. It is a moment I wouldn't have missed for the world! He looked so strange – both very ugly and exceedingly beautiful at the same time! I loved him so much instantly and wanted to stroke and cherish him and take him in my arms to hold him really close and comfort him. I was totally unaware of everything else going on till Bridget held up the placenta. I didn't see the cord at all and wish that I had because it might have helped to connect our beautiful thriving newborn creature with the baby I had grown to love in the womb – it took me ages to accept them as one and the same, it felt so much as if all my protestations and moans, and especially my unwillingness to push, had in some way killed the baby within me, and Thomas had come out of the blue by way of compensation. I feel very much that I would like to experience labour and childbirth again though, and hope that I may do it at home once again with a doctor and midwife as marvellous as Dr White and Bridget.

Untying Knots

In a lecture in the USA I described how in many traditional cultures, both in the Third World and Europe, helpers at a birth go round opening windows and doors, uncorking bottles, lifting the lids of boxes and other containers and untying all knots to enable the woman to relax and give birth to her child. This untying and opening can have a powerful effect on the labouring woman's mind. Everything in her environment is released and free and she also can open up and let her baby be born.

Marlene Muller, who wrote this poem, told me that the image of untying knots stayed with her and helped her gain insight and understanding into other areas of her life, as well as childbirth. Several weeks after the lecture she sent me this poem.

She gave birth in hospital with midwife care. In early labour, on a beautiful, restful autumn day, she walked on the beach with her husband and midwife until she was 4 cm dilated and during contractions focused on boats sailing on the ocean. The birth was a 'painful, glorious, profound experience'.

> A woman's feet curl, mouth
> tight as a locked cervix.
> She worries that her hands,
> claw-like, mean the child is trapped
> inside, will never ease through her
> to light, to your cupped hands
> waiting for the warm, waxy head.
>
> She hears sobbing, the child
> drowning in her fearful grip.
>
> Stand near her. Begin to untie
> knots, a long length of them.
> Let the rope slide in wide loops
> to the floor. Open the door,
> raise windows. Fill the room
> with the damp smell of rain,
> with spaces she can fall through,

Stroke both her legs, thigh
to foot. Her eyes close.
Soon, she will release the child
to her own cupped hands.

Twins

It is often taken for granted that a twin birth is a high-tech birth. After all, in the obstetric text books twins are listed along with abnormal labours and complications like a retained placenta. Most of the books refer to the drama of 'locked twins' which sometimes occurs when the head of a vertex baby gets stuck beside the head of an about-to-be-born breech baby. I used to worry about this myself when I was expecting twins until I discovered that this occurs so rarely that few obstetricians have ever seen it.

A twin birth can be as simple and pleasant as a straightforward birth with a single baby. Here a woman describes the completely natural birth of twins, the second of whom was breech.

At 28 weeks I asked my GP to keep me on as a 'shared care' patient, and he also promised to be at the delivery and try to ensure that my wishes were observed. So I had most of my antenatal appointments with him (short waits, pleasant waiting-room, friendly staff, unlimited opportunities to ask questions and discuss things) rather than at the hospital (long waits in cramped corridors – at least two hours normally – to see different staff each time, for a few minutes only; and rarely any offers to answer questions).

I did enjoy the pregnancy, though I got very large and very tired towards the end. But a mainly vegetarian wholefood diet helped me to avoid varicose veins, piles and other minor miseries, and I never needed vitamin or iron supplements.

Up to about 28 weeks both babies were vertex, and I was secretly hoping to not quite make it to hospital in time. At about 25 weeks I wrote a very polite letter to the consultant, deferring to his professional judgement but asking for his help in avoiding various things: continuous monitoring, analgesia (apart from gas and oxygen in late first stage), lithotomy delivery and episiotomy, etc. He discussed it with his registrar and replied that my requests were quite reasonable and he would comply as far as he could.

At 28 weeks, however, the second, smaller, twin became

breech and stayed that way. I knew that I would have to go to hospital and I also had to start a second series of arguments. No. 2 was smaller than No. 1 (though still within the normal size range for twins) and all the medical people I spoke to felt that a small breech baby (even a second-coming twin) should be born with the help of protective forceps to avoid decompression damage to the brain. Of course I wanted to do whatever was safest for the baby, but I was reluctant to believe that I could not give birth to this apparently healthy baby without damaging it. I argued with the various obstetricians in the last few weeks before the birth, and offered to deliver No. 2 in stirrups to facilitate a controlled delivery; but they all felt forceps were inevitable. My GP, bless him, mentioned the Mauriceau-Smellie-Veit manoeuvre* but even he felt that an episiotomy was probable and pointed out that if the doctor who delivered No. 2 had no experience of this manoeuvre I would have to accept forceps.

The last and most depressing phase of this argument happened when I was 39 weeks pregnant. I drove home from hospital whistling 'Everything's all right' to keep my spirits up, but feeling it wasn't very appropriate. The next morning I had twinges of what felt like indigestion at 8.30 and ignored them till 10.30 when I began to think they might be the start of a long labour. At 11.00 I considered the possibility of hospital later in the day and ate a large plate of scrambled eggs in case they tried to starve me. At 11.30 I rang Martyn (my husband) who, since he'd missed our first baby's birth because it was so quick, came home straight away. I was running a hot bath but he started timing contractions and hustled me to the car. We got to hospital about 12.20. The next few minutes went like this:

Midwife: 'Can you do a specimen dear, because you'll be in bed from now on and it'll mean a bedpan.'

Me: 'Well, I don't want to be immobilized in bed if possible . . . It's in my notes . . . could you examine me please, I've got a funny feeling . . .'

* A method of resting a hand underneath the baby's tummy as it is born and opening its mouth with a finger so that it can start breathing even before the head is delivered.

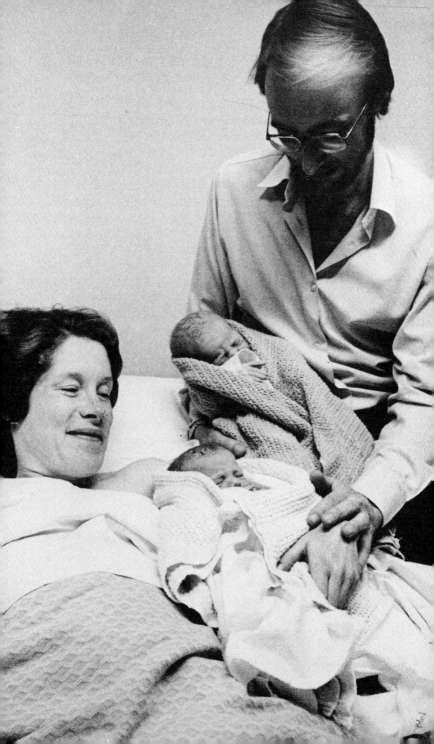

Midwife: 'In a minute dear [contraction]; yes, that's quite strong.'

Me: 'Could you ring Dr Marsh please?'

Midwife: 'All in good time dear . . .'

Me: 'And please would you examine me?'

At last she did – hardly necessary when she saw the bulging bag of waters that I had felt between my legs.

It was really lovely. Everyone stopped wheeling in machines and filling in forms and started rushing into gowns and gloves. Paediatricians and a registrar appeared from nowhere. Martyn helped me with gas and air, and between contractions I continued the forceps discussion. The registrar was a likeable young woman who said she'd do the MSV manoeuvre if she could, but put on forceps if necessary.

Ten minutes later Piers was born. Almost at once Andrew's body began to come. He hung his head for a short time, then his little blue body was lifted out over my tummy and his head slipped neatly out. I found it very exhilarating, even though I hadn't had time to collect my thoughts (which I think you need to do for second stage, if possible).

The twins arrived at 12.40 and 12.45 weighing 6 lb 6 oz and 4 lb 15 oz. Andrew needed oxygen but both were fine. I stayed in hospital for two days, then (with the agreement of a sensible paediatrician who wasn't too hung up on weight) brought them home, where they are flourishing. The big one is greedy and kicks a lot, the small one is placid and gentle; just as they were in the womb. I needed no stitches and would quite happily do the whole thing again tomorrow.

'I let my body do the work'

A woman who has had a high-tech birth the first time round and is left feeling unhappy and frustrated about what was done to her is often determined to be in control of the birth herself next time. If any intervention is proposed by the doctor which seems as if it is a replay from her previous pregnancy or labour, she becomes tense and anxious. That is what happened to this woman. Her GP found her blood pressure high at her last antenatal visit and told her she must go to hospital immediately for induction – exactly what happened before. Fortunately there were supportive women friends who came in to help her 'climb back to confidence'. She started labour naturally, and though she was not allowed to have her baby in the GP unit, and had to go into the consultant part of the hospital, she had a triumphant birth exactly the way she wanted it.

It was a beautiful sharp sunny day, and I knew on waking that our second child would be born today.

I had been aware of gentle contractions since around 4 pm the previous day. Watching Robert getting ready for work I had to assess how imminent this birth was, as he was due at a meeting in Milton Keynes (nearly three hours drive away). Our first child, John, had been induced when he was 14 days overdue so I had no experience of early labour to go by. Remembering accounts of friends' labours (while being aware that no two are alike) I decided that this very mild tightening could go on all day before anything happened. Besides, I felt that if Robert and I spent all day sitting around waiting for something to happen it probably wouldn't. So he left at 8 am promising to phone on arrival and set off back again if things had begun to move on.

John had had a very technological birth. I had been taken into hospital with high blood pressure when he was eight days overdue. My blood pressure had stabilized, but I was kept in for another five days before the induction. This was the most awful time. Being without Robert and watching other women come and go with their babies was very upsetting, so that once the induction was underway I was both demoralized and anxious to get it over with. The first seven hours of labour went well; I was sitting astride the bed and using the breathing techniques I learnt at my NCT classes. However, as I began to tire, the contractions became stronger and I began to lose control. I first resorted to gas and air, then to pethidine, and ended up with an epidural. Finally, as the second stage was delayed, John was delivered with forceps, after 14 hours of labour.

With this baby I was determined that things would be different. I managed to convince one of the GPs at my surgery that I would be a safe candidate for the local GP unit. I wanted as little intervention as possible this time. So far everything had gone well. My blood pressure had risen a little lately but now that I felt labour had begun, albeit very gently, I was feeling very optimistic.

I had an antenatal appointment that morning at my doctor's surgery. I set off at 9 am with John, feeling good. I felt well prepared for this birth. Robert and I had been to some good NCT classes and I had been attending a marvellous yoga for pregnancy class which had given me great confidence in the ability of my body to move around during labour. Sasha, a very good friend of ours, was to be with us at the birth and I had got to know both the midwives who would be likely to attend and discussed with them how I hoped things would go.

My optimism soon evaporated on arrival at the surgery. I was kept waiting for 45 minutes before being examined and was then told that my blood pressure was dangerously high and I should go straight into the consultant unit and have the baby induced! I was stunned. This was almost exactly what had happened with John. I was close to tears, but I argued that I was in the early stages of labour and had to wait for Robert's phone call before going to the hospital or he wouldn't know where I was. Finally I was told to be sure to get to the hospital by early afternoon. The rest of this day was to be a slow climb back to strength and confidence from the low I felt on leaving the surgery.

Minor things conspired to ensure that I did not make the deadline. Robert did not phone until after 1 pm and Sasha was away for the day. Other friends rallied round and it was largely due to their support that things went so well in the end. When Robert's call hadn't come by 11 am I decided to ring my friend, Germaine, who was to have John.

On hearing the whole story she suggested contacting the GP unit to see if a midwife could come out to examine me at home. I tried this, but as the GP unit had already signed me over to the consultant unit, they couldn't help. However, the conversation with Germaine had helped me to calm down and reinforced my decision not to go into hospital straight away. Tara arrived around lunchtime to collect John and take him to Germaine's for the rest of the day. She talked to me about not allowing history to repeat itself. The baby was on its way. If I concentrated on that fact and let my body do the work all would be well. She emphasized my own responsibility for how things were to go. Finally, Julie arrived and made me feel good about myself. She timed the contractions and found that they were coming every eight to ten minutes. I was doing well and looking good. I believed her and started to feel real excitement for the first time.

These contractions were still not very strong. I could ignore them and get on with organizing John's departure. He left with Tara with hardly a backward look. The implication of seeing me next with a new little brother or sister was obviously lost to him. Julie persuaded me to get out the camera before she left. She took about six shots, some of which show the anxiety I was feeling, but the last captured the good feelings which were beginning to emerge. Julie left around 2 pm and I was now able to concentrate on myself. I felt strong and relaxed and went upstairs to rest and await Robert's return.

Once I was alone I had a few qualms. Was I being foolhardy? How could I be sure that things were not going badly wrong right now? Panic began to rise, but as I felt another contraction and thought of the baby on its way all this dropped away and I was able to allow my body to get on with it. I used one of the relaxation exercises learnt at the yoga class and was soon asleep.

I awoke a couple of hours later and lay 'listening' for 15 minutes. I counted three definite but still very mild contractions. At 4 pm Robert arrived home and I was suddenly charged with energy. I wanted to get going. While getting things ready for the hospital I felt the contractions become stronger. As I became more active the gentle phase wore off and I found myself having to breathe gently through them and concentrate on relaxing.

Just before leaving I rang Germaine to let her know what was happening and to find out how John was. As I talked I was squatting on the floor and had one or two contractions which didn't interfere with the conversation, but when I stood up a really powerful one nearly took my breath away. I relaxed into it and as it died away I felt a gushing sensation and had to rush to the toilet. The mucus plug had gone. From this point I had to work hard through each contraction. They were coming every two to three minutes and getting fiercer all the time. The breathing and relaxation were working well and although I had to concentrate hard during them I was very elated.

We finally set off for the hospital at around 5.30 pm. This journey was the worst part of the whole experience. I spent it strapped into the front seat of the car. (Our NCT teacher had suggested kneeling up in the back seat but I remembered this advice too late.) It took nearly half an hour to reach the hospital, during which I was having very strong contractions every two minutes. I was relieved to be out of the car and able to move around. I could now stand, lean or squat through each contraction and did so through six or seven on the way into the building.

I was feeling calm and strong and almost totally involved in what was going on inside me. A very strong contraction caught me as I crossed reception. As I squatted and breathed through it a helpful ambulance man offered me a wheelchair! The last thing I wanted was to sit on my bum. The arrival at the labour ward took away the last traces of uncertainty. Here were professionals behaving as if everything was normal. No rush to strap me up and plug me in. I had been unaware that I had been tensing myself in readiness for a fight. But now that I wasn't to have one I was able to relax and concentrate on letting go.

The staff were very relaxed and encouraging on the whole. As I was being examined I felt able to interrupt the process in order to get to the end of the bed in a supported squat for a contraction. I was told that I was 6 cm dilated. By this time I did not much care where I was so long as I could get on with it. At the end of the examination I heard Sasha arrive, right on cue.

I remember feeling very speedy at this point, in a hurry to get to the place where the baby was to be born. My legs were beginning to feel a bit wobbly, so when someone suggested a bath I agreed, thinking it might ease the contractions and give me a chance to relax for a while. This did work for three or four contractions, the intensity of the sensations lessened and I was able to relax in between. For a while now, external considerations had been moving further away as I went more into my body. I also became more demanding of Robert and Sasha. I remember giving orders, 'more hot water', 'a drink', etc.

I had one very strong contraction which made my body feel like it was being turned inside-out. I recalled feeling this at the most difficult part of John's birth when I started to lose control. I breathed deeply through it and managed to stay relaxed with Sasha's help, but as I surfaced I remember saying, with a mixture of surprise and outrage: 'I'm not enjoying this.' Sasha reminded me quietly that the baby would soon be born. I now wanted desperately to get out of the bath but could not imagine how I was to do it. The thought of the effort required brought me to the edge of panic. With the help of Robert and Sasha I did manage to get out and dry, while working through another couple of contractions.

I found myself in the corridor and on the move again, this time to the delivery room. I felt strong again and was anxious to get settled into the place where my baby was to be born. From now on I became completely absorbed in the business of letting my body get on with giving birth. Robert and Sasha were there to deal with the external things. I felt complete confidence in them and could sink into my own experience. There were some incidents when the outside world impinged upon me: as I squatted through a contraction in the corridor a midwife tried to hurry me along with 'you can't have your baby here, dear'; a young midwife, trying to find the baby's heartbeat with a Sonicaid, and not succeeding. But I settled in a kneeling position against a pile of pillows on a chair and left all external considerations behind.

It is difficult to describe the next period of labour. The contractions were coming thick and fast. I managed to relax and let my uterus get on with the job. Since the difficult patch in the bath I had felt the need to make a noise and had no qualms about doing so. With reminders from Sasha I kept my mouth and throat relaxed and vocalized freely. The 'inside-out' quality of the contractions continued and I was using a version of the 'hoo, hoo, haa!' breath, combined with rocking rhythmically through them. Between contractions I was totally relaxed and swayed and hummed (sometimes remarkably tunefully) to myself, exchanging occasional words and glances with Robert and Sasha. This was a beautiful time. There were few interruptions from staff. It was just the three of us in a dimly lit room waiting for a new life to join us.

Suddenly it was all change. I felt the baby's head turn a corner inside me. The desire to push became overwhelming. I asked to be examined again and had to get on to the bed. Yet again I experienced real pain as a contraction came as I lay back waiting to be examined. (I hadn't the energy to get into an upright position and felt, for one contraction, what I had felt throughout John's.) I was told that I was fully dilated but with a slight lip. I immediately flipped over on to my knees, bum in the air, and stayed like this through the next few contractions.

The next thing I remember is the midwife suggesting that I could try pushing. She was on her way out and nearly missed everything. As I heard her say this another contraction was imminent and I simply came up on to my knees and let go. Suddenly I was supporting my perineum with a hard and a soft bump under my fingers (the baby's head and the membranes still intact). As a pair of gloved hands took over I dropped on to all fours for the next contraction with which the membranes broke and the head was born. Moments later there was another strong push of my uterus and the baby almost shot out. I remember hearing his loud shout of protest with relief. Somewhere the fear had stayed with me until the end.

A little awkwardly I took this insistent little being in my arms. Robert joined me and together we quietened him with our silence. Daniel arrived at 7.31, just one and half hours after we had arrived at the hospital.

This woman is sucking ice cubes during labour while her partner massages her shoulders.

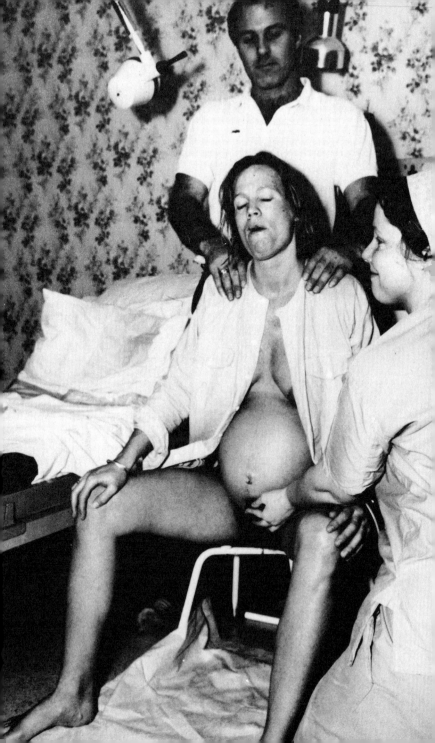

A Stitch in the Cervix

This account is interesting because it has a direct bearing on the lack of adequate research in obstetrics about many of the things that are done to women. Most obstetric practices have not been subjected to randomized controlled trials. When a woman has had a late miscarriage some obstetricians insert a stitch round the cervix (a Shirodkar suture) because they believe it helps to avoid miscarriage by holding the cervix closed. On the other hand, most women will carry to term even without the stitch. Even after two mid-pregnancy miscarriages seven out of ten have no trouble with the next pregnancy. Putting in the stitch may trigger contractions and lead to miscarriage and the stitch can cause scar tissue which makes the cervix narrower and results in very slow dilatation and a long, painful labour. This is why controlled trials of all obstetric interventions should be conducted before they become routine elements in practice.

At the beginning of this account the writer tells how she declined a scan because she realizes that research has not been done over a long enough period of time for anyone to be able to say with certainty that ultrasound does no harm. Routine ultrasound has become an accepted part of antenatal care and doctors do not usually tell women that follow-up research needs to be conducted over 50 years or so to find out if babies who are scanned in the uterus are exposed to risks which can affect them much later in their lives. On the other hand, she accepted a Shirodkar suture, the value of which is also open to question. Her labour was extremely uncomfortable and she now wonders whether its length was due to the stitch becoming embedded in her cervix.

I was told by our obstetrician to go and have a scan at 11 weeks to estimate the date the baby was due and the position of the placenta, although I had experienced no blood loss or threats to the pregnancy and we were quite confident with our dates within a few days.

After many hours of thought and discussion we decided against the scan as there seemed no particular reason relevant to the pregnancy for having it done. The obstetrician wasn't very happy that we went against his decision. Fortunately, we dealt mainly with his registrar and house officer. We found them approachable and they accepted that we were sensible enough to make our own decisions.

I was due to have a Shirodkar suture inserted because of having a miscarriage at five and a half months nine years ago. Following that miscarriage I had a Shirodkar suture inserted at my next pregnancy and gave birth to a healthy boy of 7 lb 10 oz at full term. We decided to have it inserted this time as we couldn't face the possibility of a miscarriage. The pregnancy went well and I felt extremely fit and had a marvellous feeling of well-being. The estimated date of delivery was August 3rd.

On July 19th Graham and I prepared walls for decorating and on the 20th we went for a three-quarter-mile walk. On the 21st I woke at 7 am, having irregular contractions between seven and twenty minutes apart. The stitch was due to be removed the next day. We contacted the hospital and they asked us to go and book in, which we did at 10.30 am. They decided to remove the stitch. It had become embedded in my cervix and the pain was extreme. It didn't help having contractions and a heavy-handed registrar who took about 15 minutes to remove it.

After this I was monitored for an hour and so was our baby, a practice we didn't find helpful as the equipment wasn't functioning properly and we kept getting odd readings or the machine cut out altogether. My own feelings were much more helpful. Irregular contractions lasted throughout the day and we felt more and more despondent as we wanted to be at home at this stage and were worried in case they would suggest an induction. At 9 pm the house officer came to see us and was very sympathetic to our feelings, saying to return home as he felt happy that we were sensible enough to return to the hospital if contractions became more frequent.

We returned home full of relief to be in our own house, had a shared bath and went to bed. The contractions were still coming and there had been no let up since I woke that morning. I dozed slightly but felt increasingly aware that they were getting stronger and more frequent. I went to the toilet and there was a definite blood-stained discharge. I 'watched' the contractions and each time I went to the toilet there was more of the blood-stained discharge. I woke Graham and he timed the contractions. They were five minutes apart so we decided to telephone the hospital and they said to go back in. We arrived at 3 am.

They examined me and I was only 4–5 cm dilated. I was so disappointed as contractions were still coming regularly. For the next few hours Graham and I were left alone, apart from the occasional check on blood pressure or vaginal examination. It was nice to be left alone with Graham, he was so loving and supportive, but I was becoming more and more despondent as I seemed to be taking so long to dilate and make progress and by now was feeling exhausted. I had been relying on my breathing exercises up until then but was getting desperate and feeling that I couldn't cope any longer because of the sheer exhaustion. I asked for gas and oxygen but it wasn't much help as it distracted me from the breathing and I felt confused. On reflection, I realize this was the transition stage. I told Graham that I must have some pethidine. After another internal examination the midwife told me that I was 6 cm dilated and stuggested breaking my waters. We had been very reluctant to before, and although we felt no pressure from her agreed to have it done. We also asked about pethidine and she said she wasn't sure if it would be worth it at this stage, but as I said I was feeling it was difficult to cope she agreed.

Everything went absolutely haywire after that, the contractions were coming fast and furious, overlapping each other with no let-up and I felt mixed up. Then suddenly I felt the urge to push and called the midwife. She yelled to her assistant, then examined me and guided me through the pushing. She asked Graham to put on some gloves so that he could deliver the baby. He had great difficulty as his hands were so sweaty and she said, 'Oh don't worry'. With that Graham held the head and helped to deliver Timothy on to my tummy. He was so beautiful and healthy, the tears were rolling down Graham's face. It was such a beautiful and emotional experience – which we had shared completely. Graham was given the scissors and allowed to cut the cord.

Timothy was born at 9.19 am after me being in recognizable labour for nearly 27 hours. He weighed 6 lb 9 oz. We came home at 5 pm that day and apart from the ambulance journey back we were together all the time. (Graham followed in the car.) It was all a beautiful experience and I felt very well and strong afterwards.

Miscarriage

Miscarriage is a neglected subject. There are antenatal classes, books, films, TV and radio programmes and postnatal support groups in the community to help you approach birth and cope with the experience after, but very little about miscarriage.

Women are expected to go through it alone and snap back afterwards as if nothing had happened. Yet for many it is a traumatic experience – and this even when it occurs early in pregnancy. This is the story of one woman who lost two babies when they were already fully formed and almost viable.

At the grand old age of 41 years I have just suffered my third miscarriage at 23 weeks. This time I had a suture put in the cervix, but it failed as it became infected, which started my labour, despite my living the life of a nun throughout my pregnancy.

You can imagine how upset we were, because it really was a last-chance pregnancy. We hadn't planned it which made it all the more of a pleasant surprise. We agonized for weeks as to whether to have the amniocentesis test done or not in case it started a miscarriage. However, I had it done and survived it. I had to wait five weeks to be told everything was all right and it was a healthy baby girl. My baby was born feet first and had died about an hour before she was born. This time we saw her and held her. I can't remember her very well now, I couldn't see her properly through my tears, but they gave us a photograph of her. It has helped me quite a lot.

I lost my first baby when I was just 20 years old, then I was told, 'Don't look, you don't want any nasty memories.' I thought I must have given birth to a monster! It wasn't until a nurse said to me, 'Did you want a little boy? What a shame. He was a lovely baby,' that I felt a little better and I've remembered those words for 21 years.

We were lucky some 21 years ago as there were babies to adopt, although even then it was difficult. We adopted a boy who is now 18 and a girl who is 16. They are super kids and we are all very close. I feel fulfilled as a mum, but not as a human being. I wanted to know what a baby of mine and my husband would look like. However, I now look at my little photo and know she would have been the image of my husband.

I lost my other baby 13 years ago. After we had adopted I became pregnant again. As well as miscarrying, I didn't seem to get pregnant very often. We haven't taken precautions at all during our married life, but still only managed to get pregnant three times. The doctors couldn't find out why. That baby was whisked away. It was alive – I do know that – but I was never told even its sex. At the time I was too sick at heart even to ask. The worst thing is other people's attitudes. After I lost my first and still hadn't managed to get pregnant again after three years, one 'friend' said to me: 'I don't know what you are making such a fuss about, you've only had a miscarriage. Lots of people do.' It was as though I had lost a clot of blood, not a little person. She went on to say: 'You are young, you have plenty of time on your side.'

Well, I'm not young any more and I've never stopped trying or hoping for a baby. Twenty-one years must be some sort of record. For the first time in our married lives we are using birth control as my husband says we just can't go through it all again, however remote the chances. My doctor said recently, 'Get yourself sterilized. You'll never carry a baby to term' – a little unfeeling I thought, although I am an old hand at coming to terms with this special kind of grief.

Perhaps in my turn I could help someone else get through their pain. Mine then would not have all been in vain.

The first time I cried every day for a year. The second time I didn't show any emotion at all. I sort of went into shock, but I had two small children to look after and that helped. On the anniversary of the day I lost it I cried all day, not for myself, but for the little being that never had a life. This last time the feeling of grief was deep inside me. My husband and I held each other very close and cried and cried. I cannot describe the awful pain inside me. We knew it must be our final try and that our hopes would never be realized. My kids were wonderful. I think it helped them understand how much we wanted them all those years ago. It broke me up to see my poor old mum and dad (now nearly 80 years old) crying for me in my loss. I couldn't bear to cause them more pain. It was dreadful. My 'macho' son put his arms round me and we cried together. My daughter hid the half-finished baby jacket she was making; she was so looking forward to a little baby sister. She had fussed round me for weeks, making me rest. It brought us all very close and I realized what nice children I have, which is difficult to remember sometimes as we go through the traumatic teenage years!

None of my babies have a grave. They all had a post-mortem. You see, they said it might help someone else! Do unbaptized babies go to heaven? If I were a Christian it would be a comfort.

A Stillbirth

Few books on childbirth really face up to the possibility – remote though it is – that a baby may die. Many birth educators are reluctant to explore feelings in their classes about death and what will happen if a baby is stillborn, because they are anxious that they will make pregnant women unnecessarily frightened. Yet in Western countries roughly one baby in every hundred dies before labour starts, during childbirth or soon after.

No woman is prepared for the tumultuous emotions around child-birth if she has not also contemplated how she might feel if her baby dies and has some idea of what she would want to happen. In many ways, of course, we can never prepare ourselves psychologically for the shock and distress of an experience like that. We can never rehearse and plan with any sense of reality. But listening to women who have themselves been through this, understanding something of what the experience was for them, can help open our minds to the possibility and give us strength and confidence to cope with the loss of a baby.

In the past, the care provided for a mother whose baby died has often been terribly inadequate. She has had no one to talk to about her feelings and members of hospital staff have avoided her because of their own distress, embarrassment and inability to cope.

Deborah's baby died before she went into labour. Here she describes the kind of care from midwives which enabled her to turn an experience full of sadness into one which she remembers with joy because of the genuine understanding and kindness she received.

My baby died in utero at about 32 weeks. Labour was induced. This should have been a ghastly episode. However, for reasons I still cannot understand it turned out to be a positive birth experience, memorable and meaningful. The staff were totally sympathetic and made me feel that the birth of my baby was no less important than anybody else's.

Induction with prostaglandins is not pleasant – I had bad shivers and vomiting – but pain was totally blotted out with an epidural regularly topped up and the midwives were full of loving care and kind words. My mother was allowed to be present all the time.

The birth actually happened while I was asleep. When I woke

up my mother saw that the head had appeared and called the midwife. I saw the baby but didn't want to hold it. I will never forget the midwife wrapping the baby in a cloth and cuddling it with a lovely smile on her face. To her it didn't matter that the baby was dead and slightly macerated. That was lovely. Had I wanted I could have asked for the baby later.

I spent the night in my original single room on the antenatal ward. Everybody was again very sympathetic and visiting was unrestricted. I was allowed my privacy, although the nurse also made it clear that she was ready to listen if I wanted to talk. When I did want to discuss it she gave me time to sob in between without either being embarrassed or trying to cheer me up by changing the subject. She certainly could have taught the chaplain a thing or two!

I would have no qualms about a delivery at this hospital now. I would feel confident that I had put myself in loving hands, concerned to do the best for me and the baby in terms both of our physical health and mental happiness.

A Father Writes about Stillbirth

The death of a baby arouses overwhelming emotions in a father. Men are often unprepared for the depth of their feelings. There may be ready sympathy for the woman who has lost a child but less awareness of what it means to the father. Here a man tells about his experience of the stillbirth of his daughter in the eighth month of a trouble-free pregnancy.*

I first found out that I would be a father early one summer morning when my wife's monthly ritual of taking a home pregnancy test showed that another life had started. There was one ring at the bottom of the glass container. Cheryl and I tried for a year and a half to conceive; I never imagined it would take so long. Two people, both in their thirties, worried about such things as age and childbirth. For a long while I thought something might be wrong. Now, I was going to be a father for the first time.

I felt emotions I could not identify or even talk about, as I watched life swell in Cheryl's stomach. There was a little person beginning life and I was beginning fatherhood. I read books, chapters, articles, anything that would give me information about what was actually happening week by week. I wanted to know as much as I could about this new little person.

One night Cheryl started the 'kick game,' gently tapping on her belly and feeling a responding kick. When I felt that first kick against my own hand, I put my cheek to Cheryl's stomach and said, 'Hello baby, this is Daddy.' Another kick. I had found a way to be a part of the daily growth of this baby. I told anyone who would listen that I talked to my child every night.

With the anticipation that all expectant parents feel, we planned for and dreamed about this baby's life. We prepared the baby's room, remembering from our own childhoods the safe haven always available in 'my room.' Grandma's front-

* This account by Kenneth R. Freeston first appeared in the *New York Times* as 'Hello Baby, This is Daddy' and is reproduced with their kind permission.

porch rocker would be perfect for nursing the baby. I took it out of the attic, stripped off the old paint and had a new seat made. I painted the room and Cheryl started to stencil a teddy-bear pattern around the four walls. Together we searched for the perfect crib, the ideal changing table and stroller, all the things that two people buy when the delivery date seems too far away to be real.

One night, at the start of the eighth month, baby Jennifer was still. Asleep, I thought. Days later Cheryl had regular contractions. We rushed to the hospital, expecting a premature birth, worrying about incubators, and praying the baby would survive the labour and delivery. We had not yet started the childbirth classes, but somehow that did not matter. The nurse attached a fetal heart monitor to the same place on Cheryl's belly where I put my cheek every night. Silence.

A sudden and undiagnosed onset of severe toxaemia destroyed the placenta's ability to give nourishment. Jennifer's heart stopped.

No one actually said, 'Your baby is dead.' They said only that they could not find a heartbeat.

In situations like these, the doctors said, it is best for the mother to deliver the fetus naturally. Cheryl's contractions continued through the night and she delivered the baby the next morning. It seems cruelly unfair that a mother has to endure childbirth to bear a heart that does not beat. For Cheryl, there would be no crying baby after the pain of labour and delivery. Just more silence.

'It was a little girl,' the nurse said. Gone, for a moment, was the rage. I held baby Jennifer Cheryl in my arms, calmed by the wonder of birth. I knew she was dead, but somehow, all I felt was love for this little two-pound baby, perfect in every physiological sense, starved by a placenta that could no longer give her life. This was the only time we would have together as mother, father and daughter. Cheryl and I held each other, numbed by the truth we cradled.

There is no preparation for the loss of a child, even an unborn child. Instead of celebrating the joy and wonder of birth, we were thrust into the disorienting despair brought by death. Cheryl, as Jennifer's mother, feels a pain that only a mother can feel. Milk fills her breasts with no baby to suckle them. Her stomach is flat again, making the swelling seem distant and imagined. She weeps with feelings of failure and inadequacy. A father's pain is no less intense, just different.

In my life I have taught about death and dying, consoled friends who lost family members, and grieved over the deaths of a close friend and my mother. None of that helps me face Jennifer's death. All around me there are parents who bear children with ease. I fight back the envy and jealousy I feel seeing a newborn being held in a parent's loving arms. Catalogues for children's toys come in the mail and I cry. I wish for the time when I had never heard of toxaemia. An emptiness aches inside all the time.

Expressions of grief, sorrow and support help for a while. The clergy tells us that we each live three lives, one before birth, one on earth, and one after death, that God's love for us will sustain us and that God is with us in our pain and suffering. Friends visit, call and send notes. They tell us that words are inadequate, that their thoughts and prayers are with us and that they share our pain and loss. Everyone offers to do something, to help us in any way we want. Friends grieve, too. They know that Jennifer's death is an unexplainable mystery, unfair, and that only the passage of time will allow us to heal. They offer hope that we will someday be wonderful parents, consoling thoughts that Jennifer is now in a place of greater love and peace than can ever be found here and that Jennifer's death reminds them to cherish every moment with their own children.

We ask the doctors question after question. Was there anything we did to cause this? Would an earlier medical intervention have saved her life? Could she have survived as a two-pound baby? Why did it happen? Will it happen again? This endless questioning, like other activities, keeps us engaged with Jennifer, but it will end soon and we will face the loneliness of a half-painted nursery.

I am learning that healing is only delayed by feelings of anger, jealousy and denial. Grieving is a personal process and for me I will not be able to begin to heal until I allow myself to grieve. I search for questions that express my fears, knowing that answers do not exist for most of them. I talk about every feeling I can identify and I cry whenever I feel the tears approach. I lie at Cheryl's side for hours at a time.

There is truth to the beliefs that time heals and that distance brings perspective. Eventually I will be comforted by finishing the teddy bears on the nursery walls, stocking the bathroom with the newer home pregnancy test and waiting for another summer morning. In time Cheryl will play the kick game again, and I will say 'Hello baby, this is Daddy.' The next child will be a second child, not a replacement, not a substitute, and I await the joy of holding that breathing, kicking, crying baby. And when I think of the future in this way, I am trapped by the familiarity of these hopes.

In some small way the grief is lessened when I remember that I am already a father.

Natural Induction

Going past your due date and knowing that you are in line for induction of labour can be worrying. You feel your body is going to let you down. You may be anxious that if labour is induced you will be compelled to have the whole high-tech package and that all your plans for birth the way *you* want will be ignored. This is how Amanda felt when, aged 39 and pregnant with her second baby, the obstetrician gave her a firm deadline for induction when she was more than two weeks past her 'due date'.

She rang me when I was the guest on a phone-in radio programme and I suggested that she and her partner tried natural induction. They should set the scene for relaxed and luxurious love-making and use sexual arousal, intercourse with penetration as deep as possible as she lay on her back with her legs raised and resting on her partner's shoulders, and prolonged nipple stimulation afterwards. They tried it and it worked. She fell asleep after happy and passionate love-making and woke early in the morning with contractions coming thick and fast. They reached the hospital 20 minutes before the birth of her baby. Here is Amanda's story:

During that long hot Easter I began to think he liked it so much in there he would never come out. Angus was 17 days overdue. I felt mostly fine. Sometimes anxious that he was no longer alive. Sometimes dejected and despairing. Days passed with just Tiffany and me in the garden when I'd think Angus should have been with us too. I thought that a lot. A bit like living on borrowed time I suspect. A little anxiously I wondered what Tiffany would feel and how a new baby would affect our relationship.

I did not feel so fine after the much-dreaded and despised induction was mentioned. I felt panicked, depressively counting each day that 'nothing happened', putting pressure on myself for self-help, gentle persuasion, anything to get him out at his own sweet pace before they did it at theirs. Above all, I wanted to be responsible for my own delivery, to be in control, able to cope with Angus's birth as I had with Tiffany's: walking around when I liked, on all fours when I liked, lying on cold tiles when

I liked, using The Breathing, without drugs and with my NCT-induced confidence that I could do it. I did not want to be chained to bed, wired up like a laboratory animal, helpless, with all that was happening to me totally beyond my control, and in their hands, with more pain, more drugs, more worrying about the baby's ability to keep pace with the technology, and more risk of more intervention. I did not want to lie passively on my back and suffer with an active audience.

I'd been told several times to get back into bed shortly before Tiffany was born, as no one believed I was in labour when I was actually 7 cm dilated! The last place I wanted to be then was *in bed*, so I paced, I leaned, I lay flat on the floor, up and down, out and about, not flat out. No thank you. I did not want to be induced.

How was I to avoid this looming fate? Impulsively, I telephoned Radio 4's programme on childbirth to ask Sheila Kitzinger's advice on coaxing Angus out. We should make love with my legs high in the air, thus allowing the semen to thoroughly cover the cervix as the hormone prostaglandin, which is present in semen, is the one used in the induction procedure, and encourages contractions.

We can recommend this method. At 5.45 am, on the beautiful sunny Sunday morning of May 6th, two days before the dreaded induction, we began our journey to Carmarthen, with me on all fours in the back of the car, swearing because I'd forgotten to remove Tiffany's car seat. I breathed, how I breathed! I secretly feared we had left it too late. Thinking this, and with contractions growing rapidly stronger, I remember starting to say, 'I *think* I'm having a contraction,' when up until then I'd been saying 'I'm having a contraction'. The more certain it became, the more I seemed determined to doubt it.

I had a contraction holding on to the seat in the hospital park. We flagged down a casualty nurse to beg for a wheelchair and lift. 'They like you to walk dear,' she said. Now I could hardly move. Snail's pace I shuffled, a step at a time, across the car park, knowing I'd never make it. I kept seeing all those stairs. Endless flights. The casualty nurse pursued us, seeing my state, and suggested waiting for a porter. How long? Ten to twenty minutes. I didn't dare. Like a maze in a child's book, when I thought I'd made it, a few more blind alleys had been added. I staggered, I climbed, I stopped and breathed. I'd forgotten to tap out my tune. I always thought I would.

Two sleepy nurses nearing shift change, soon in top gear. Time 6.55 am. One fumbled with my identification band. 'I want to push,' I mumbled. She fumbled some more as the words sunk in, gave up, zoomed me down the corridor to the delivery room. Hoisting me on to the bed, she asked, 'How do you feel about being delivered by a medical student?' Don't go away I thought. 'No,' I managed to say, cackling to myself, 'there won't be time for that.'

Fully dilated, heartbeat fine. 'That's good,' I heard Pete say. I pushed a handful of times, each push being well rewarded with head, shoulders and rest of Angus's little body emerging eagerly and responsively to greet us. How quickly, once decided, he did it! Time 7.15 am. 'It's a boy,' Pete said of the dried up, wizened, overcooked little prune that was our son.

Six hours later Angus met Tiffany and we took him home in the sunshine to Tess our dog and the three cats, Squidgy, Gippo and Tiddler.

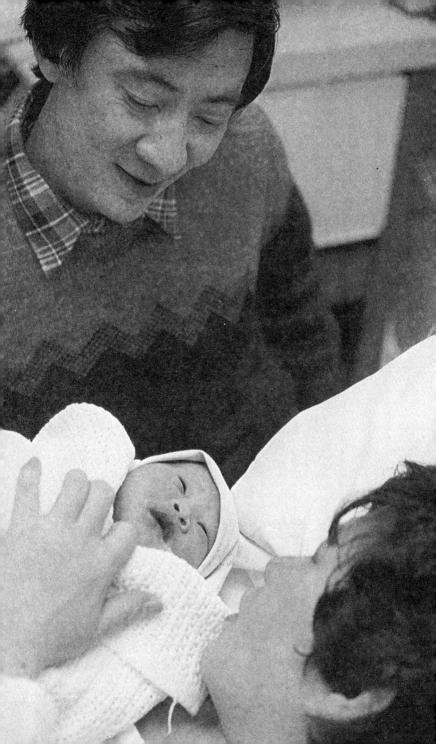

A Backache Labour

Backache labours, when the baby is in a posterior position, with the spine lying parallel to the mother's spine and the hard back of the baby's head pressing against the small of her back, are often tedious, tiring and painful. However excited a woman is when labour starts, her morale tends to drop as hour after hour passes without apparent progress – only constant backache, which is often so strong that contractions seem nothing beside it.

The woman writing here had experienced two labours like this and was dreading another. It turned out that this labour followed the same pattern. The difference was that she was in her own home, her husband was with her throughout and she had the kind of loving, understanding care she wanted. In spite of constant pain she found she was able to cope well with it and felt the birth was a deeply satisfying experience.

My third child was born at home, eight days late and weighed 8 lb 10 oz. I went to NCT classes this time – from about four to seven months – oh, and what a lot of old buried memories it stirred up! I was frankly terrified of all that pain again and didn't feel I could cope with another labour like the others – but this time I didn't want to take any drugs either. Instead I wanted my husband to be with me. I'd felt very separated from him, a feeling lasting for months after the others – he thought I'd been to hospital for a baby just like any other woman – but I knew I'd had a really traumatic and profound experience that was far from routine, but wouldn't share it with him. Also, as the pregnancy was an accident I wanted him to be as close as possible to the little one so that he would never feel resentful of him. My feelings were also complicated by the fact that he had a vasectomy when I was about 18 weeks pregnant – it was like putting all your eggs in one basket! The two older boys, nearly ten and eleven and a half, were interested, curious and very involved – indeed, they wanted to be there but I didn't want that.

The other complication was that at 31 weeks (and 12 stone) I fell off my bike – or to be exact, went over the handlebars, and was very bruised and needed stitches in my face. That was not only a shock, but the backache that had been bothering me all through the pregnancy was even worse, my ribs were bruised, my breasts black and blue (really). Fortunately it didn't precipitate labour. My GP came and stitched me up at home and let me rest there, for which I was grateful. I healed well, except for the back.

My midwife was marvellous. She was of the opinion that a lot of babies could safely be born at home. She was so calm and matter-of-fact and quietly competent, never rushing. She wanted to know all the details of my previous labours and admitted I was likely to be in for another long, slow labour, particularly when we found this baby was a posterior presentation!

A few days before the baby was due I started to have mild contractions which lasted an hour or two, then went off. Braxton-Hicks I assumed.* Then on the day I was due I had quite strong contractions every 20 minutes for about four hours, and the same the next day. They always went off at night or when I had a bath and was resting.

When I was about four days late I reported a small weight loss to my doctor and told him of the contractions. He immediately said that he didn't want me to go more than a week late without being induced. I was very upset, as I assumed I'd have a fortnight's grace and did not want an induction. Thanks to the NCT I'd come to terms with the idea of labour and birth but didn't feel I could face induction too! I'd also read so much my head was whirling! My midwife read my copy of *Birth without Violence*† and agreed to leave the umbilical cord till it had stopped pulsing and to do everything quietly with dim lights. I'd also told her not to bring any pethidine with her as I intended to manage without, although she did bring some gas and air. She was so kind that my main worry was trying to time it while she was on duty. It was no accident that my blood pressure always showed up higher at the doctor's surgery than when she came to the house for a check-up.

* See Glossary
† Frédérick Leboyer (Fontana, 1977).

I had contractions, quite strong, all that weekend, every 15 to 20 minutes, going off in the night. On Monday morning, however, they were still there so I phoned the midwife and asked her to come and see if I couldn't have an enema. At about 11 am she arrived, then examined me and said I was dilating slightly. I had my enema and hot bath and she went away about noon – I was now officially in labour. Contractions became stronger and more frequent through the afternoon. I whipped round the house making bread and a meal for the evening and tidying up. She came back about 4.30 pm, examined me and found a hand in the way. She was able to tickle the hand so the baby pulled it back and the head engaged properly. In the course of this the waters broke and the head dropped into the posterior presentation we hoped it was moving out of. Contractions were down to every four or five minutes lasting a minute and I retired to bed.

The midwife stayed with me, except for having the meal I'd prepared – so different from the earlier labours where I'd been on my own for hours. At 8 pm I was violently sick, and the contractions were lasting between two and four minutes, coming at irregular intervals. My top level breathing just wasn't enough to cope with the strength of the contractions, and my midwife taught me another procedure, which involved snatching in the air and blowing it out. It helped and she did it with me. At 8.30 pm I was examined again, and had dilated another centimetre so she phoned the doctor to say I *was* making progress. (Slow!) He then went off duty and a relief doctor whom I hadn't met was in charge. I was offered gas and air but refused it. I don't think I could have managed it and breathe too. The backache was continuous and almost unendurable and I couldn't even bear to move to let my husband do his back-rubbing routine. He came in at 9 pm to stay, after putting the boys to bed and I just clung to him.

From then on I wanted to push very strongly but was nowhere near dilated so had a hard time of it to hold back. The midwife explained it was the baby's head creating the terrible continuous back pain. I couldn't feel the contractions starting because of already being in pain. She helped by resting her hand on my stomach and telling me as they started.

About 11 pm I was dilated enough to push but there was no satisfaction in it because of the continuous pain. I couldn't really time the pushes to the contractions properly. At about 11.20 pm a strange doctor walked in. He'd just come because he liked babies, he said, but there was no question that my midwife was still in charge. I took an unfair but immediate dislike to him because he was outside the three of us who'd been experiencing the whole process so far. Also he smelt of cigarettes and I didn't want him breathing on the baby!

At about 11.40 pm she was about to turn the baby's head so that pushing was more effective. When she said it wouldn't be long and to get the overhead light off, the doctor said, 'Oh, a Leboyer birth – don't we have music?' and I remember saying, 'No – just silence,' rather tartly! Then I pushed for three contractions and the baby's head was born. As soon as he was born he was put on my abdomen. Slowly, over a couple of minutes, he went pink and breathed on his own – no crying, no trauma. We were all born again, just watching him become conscious, breathe and open his eyes.

It wasn't until about five minutes after that we realized we hadn't looked to see if he was a boy or girl – so we looked under the towel and he was a boy! By then we were all laughing. After the pulsing stopped the cord was cut and he fed straight away.

I could have got up and danced the rest of the night! As soon as I was cleaned up my husband woke up the boys to tell them. They came in and we had a party. He made us all some cocoa and cut a birthday cake I'd baked. The boys had chosen the baby's name – Danny – so they were thrilled.

The midwife checked the baby over. He got a rating of nine on the Apgar scale. She finally left us about 4 am. My husband fell into bed beside me and was asleep quickly. I was so excited I didn't sleep a wink, with him breathing steadily on one side of me and the baby whiffling and snorting on the other. I was on cloud nine. I felt as if 'my cup runneth over' I was so happy. I couldn't wait to feed the baby again. We really got off to a good start.

I couldn't bear to put the baby down for long and he just fed and slept in my arms. I was in no hurry to take up the reins again and hardly went downstairs for a week!

I was left feeling so lucky and grateful I was able to go to the NCT classes, which were tremendously important to me even though I often found them a bit upsetting and could never sleep after them! They helped me prepare. And although the labour was, if anything, worse than my previous two experiences, I felt much better about it during and after. Having my husband there this time helped, of course, but it was not only that. I really was more 'with it'; my mind was sharp and I knew what was happening.

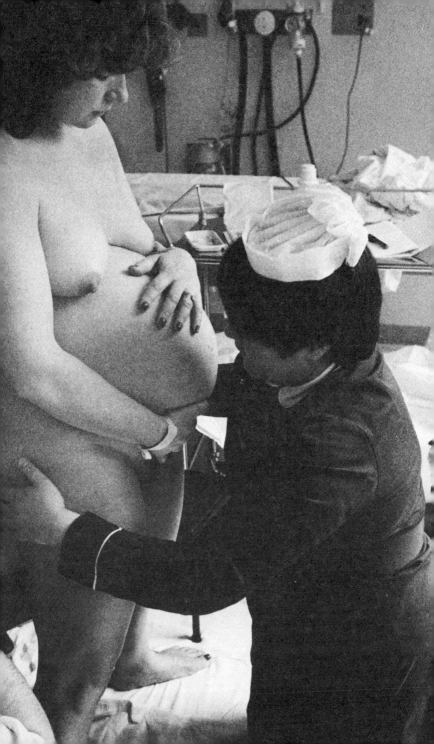

Feelings of Failure

Here a woman expresses her feelings about a Caesarean section and wonders whether it was really necessary. Caesarean section rates in England and Wales rose from 7.4 per cent in 1977 to 12.5 per cent in 1986. In the USA, rates in many hospitals are as high as 30 per cent. Private patients in Britain are more than twice as likely to have Caesareans as those having their babies on the National Health Service.

The author of this birth account now feels her emergency Caesarean section might have been caused by the high degree of obstetric intervention in her labour, including artificial rupture of the membranes, drugs to stimulate the uterus, continual electronic fetal monitoring and an epidural.

I had a baby daughter by emergency Caesarean section after a long labour – one which was constantly interfered with.

I am very puzzled that I needed the Caesarean section as my pregnancy was completely trouble-free. At four months I was wardrobe mistress and acting in an amateur open-air production of *The Taming of the Shrew* and at eight and three-quarter months was helping with props for a production of *Blithe Spirit*!

I went into natural labour at about midday on 12th December. By the time my husband returned home contractions were coming regularly every 20 minutes. As the evening wore on the time between contractions grew shorter and by 11 pm they were coming every ten minutes. My husband took me to the hospital and I was admitted at about 11.30 pm. At 12 midnight the contractions were every five minutes and that is how they stayed throughout the night and the next morning. I was not anxious or worried. My husband was with me, I was looking forward to the birth and we were both excited. I had attended antenatal classes and was as prepared as I could be for the unknown.

During the coming and going of the staff I heard someone say I was not really in labour yet – it felt like it! At 12 midday a senior midwife with a trainee midwife came to break my waters, 'to speed things up a bit'. The trainee was to do this and I was given gas and air while she attempted to break the waters. Up until now I had been coping with pain without any drugs or any help other than breathing.

The trainee midwife could not break the waters and did not really know what she was supposed to be doing. She said so to the senior midwife; I heard her! I continued to breathe the gas and air which removed any pain. At this point I was being talked about as if I were just someone who happened to be there. The two midwives could not break the waters so I was left until 4 pm when a gynaecologist came to do the job.

By this time I found I could no longer bear the pain without the gas and air and was using it continuously. The gynaecologist, a man, called me 'ma'am' and talked about me as if I were some kind of deaf half-wit, out of my mind with fear of pain – which should be expected in childbirth of course! I was not too happy by now, as you can imagine. He did break the waters, although I felt nothing, and nothing more happened. I was put on a drip to accelerate 'things' and then a 'piggy-back' drip, whatever that is – still no baby!

At about 10 pm I was given an epidural and put on a fetal monitor. Around this time I really lost track of proceedings except that I watched the monitor for the fetal heart – which stopped and started alarmingly.

At about 3.30 am I was prepared for an emergency Caesarean section due to fetal distress. This was carried out and at 3.58 am, and after nearly 40 hours of labour, my daughter was safely delivered. She has proved to be an exceptionally bright child, walking steadily and alone at nine and a half months, talking well at 12 months and now at two years quick, intelligent and perhaps somewhat precocious.

My daughter was bottlefed by staff after birth as I was woozy still. I was never asked if I wanted to breastfeed and only realized *two days after she was born* that nothing had been done about it. Then I breastfed, with *much* trouble and little help from staff, but for only six weeks, when I got a lump in my breast and my GP told me to stop. I realize now I could have carried on breastfeeding – that is with hindsight.

Very little seems to be written about the psychological effect a Caesarean can have upon a woman – guilt, anxiety and failure. The experience shattered me and my confidence in myself as a woman and gave me a feeling of failure at not being able to perform the function for which I, a woman, was intended – having a baby – and then having such trouble breastfeeding. It hurts terribly to read glowing articles in magazines about wonderful births. I realize that Caesarean sections are an emergency procedure, but I sometimes wonder if mine was really necessary.

Although my own experience was not what I had anticipated, the result, my beautiful daughter, was and is the most precious thing in my life – in our lives I should say, because my husband shares my feelings. We have not had the desire for other children, nothing to do with the experience, but our daughter completed a strong and deep love between us. I sometimes wonder, and cannot believe, that other people feel as we do – and cannot help feeling too that our love for each other is unique – almost fearful in its intensity.

Frustration and Anger

Some obstetricians assume that every breech baby should be delivered by elective (planned in advance) Caesarean section. Here a woman successfully challenges that view and is allowed to start labour normally. But then a great deal of intervention takes place and things go wrong.

Problems begin with artificial stimulation of her uterus because her cervix is dilating slowly – and from this point on there is a cascade of intervention. Machines, of course, do not always work perfectly. And even when they do, their efficiency depends on people using them appropriately and being able to interpret data correctly. Unfortunately this woman's uterus was over-stimulated by oxytocin administered through an intravenous drip, resulting in a slowing of the fetal heart and danger to the baby. Those looking after her did not realize that the electronic monitor was set at the wrong speed. The rate of contractions was three times that which was apparently recorded. She had an emergency Caesarean section. Next time she has a baby she is determined that she will labour in her own way and her own time and feels that she can be sure of this only if she has her baby at home.

My GP examined me at 35 weeks and said that she thought my baby was lying in a breech position and put this on my co-op card. (My husband, who is a doctor, had said this for weeks.) My tummy muscles were very firm which made it rather more difficult to be certain. I was due to have a scan (routine under that particular consultant) two days later. This confirmed the breech position. I was terribly upset because, even though I had never expected it to happen to me, I was aware from my reading that a great many obstetricians believe that the only safe way to deliver a breech is by Caesarean.

I had an appointment at the hospital five days later. The consultant examined me and said that everything was okay. This is where I made the mistake which I have regretted ever since – telling him that on the scan the baby was breech. From that moment on what had been a very happy pregnancy was turned upside down, taken out of my hands and made extremely unhappy. I was put down for twice-weekly 24-hour urine collections and fetal monitoring sessions. When I asked him what the policy was for breech births, he said that it would be an elective section. I left without saying anything, partly because I knew that I would start to cry and partly because I wanted to discuss with my husband what we were going to do.

I won't go into the feelings of just being booked in for an operation rather than giving birth. I was so confused. I couldn't see any reason for an elective section as I was so healthy and we knew from the scan that the baby was small.

Roger (my husband) and I made it our business in the next three days to find out as much as possible about breech delivery and Caesarean section. We spoke to doctors, midwives and our NCT teacher and came to the conclusion that we wanted a trial of labour. The consultant was not amused, to say the least. He tried to blackmail us emotionally, was very rude to me and succeeded in making me very frightened. Fortunately, he was on holiday when I went into labour and his senior registrar was slightly more approachable, although not sympathetic.

A brief account of my labour is as follows:

11 am	membranes ruptured – slight trickle all day and night.
2 am	very strong, painful contractions every eight minutes.
3 am	into hospital V.E. [vaginal examination] – 3 cm dilated – monitored – all well.
9 am	V.E. 4 cm – told not dilating very quickly – could feel foot – better go on drip. Letting them do this was my biggest mistake, as I now strongly feel that it would have taken me a long time to dilate, since the presenting part of a foot on the cervix was not helping nature as much as if the head had been the presenting part. I was taken to the delivery room, put on a drip and continually monitored. I lost control of the contractions for a while. The monitor showed everything to be okay, but of course I was now completely immobile.
	Various people kept looking at the monitor and saying that I wasn't contracting very much and that

115

they'd better turn up the drip, and this was done several times.

11.05 am   V.E. 6 cm – turned drip up yet again. By this time, with the contractions coming so quickly and so many people interfering with me I had completely lost control. I asked for an epidural (I had decided to have an epidural anyway as there was always the possibility of a section and I didn't want to be given a general anaesthetic).

12.30 pm   V.E. 8 cm – signs of fetal distress – told have to be prepared for section.

At this point the sister came in, looked at the monitor and asked the student midwife why no one had realized that it was on the wrong speed – recording contractions three times slower than the rate they were actually happening. This is the thing that I have felt so very bitter about ever since. No one ever asked me how often I was having contractions or how long they were lasting for. They all – senior registrar, registrar, midwives, anaesthetist – relied on the monitor and not one of them realized that it was on the wrong speed. It was too late now. My baby was having type II dips.*

My baby was delivered by Caesarean section at 1.20 pm and although I was awake and saw her being lifted out it was just a hazy dream because my blood pressure dropped rapidly as they topped up my epidural. Very sadly it has remained a haze in my mind.

I adore my baby, she is nine months now, crawling, climbing and absolutely beautiful. But the birth and events leading to it are still a very unhappy memory for me. I bitterly resent the mismanagement and intervention, both of which I believe are to blame for making a Caesarean necessary. I know that I should have put my foot down and asked them not to put a drip up but when you are in labour it's hard to be assertive. I

* See Glossary

116

feel so angry that those people may have taken away my chance of ever experiencing a normal birth.

We had always planned to have a second baby at home and after my experiences in hospital I feel even more strongly that this is the right place for me.

This woman wrote to me later, after the birth of her second child, saying that it had been a very happy experience – completely different from the first baby's birth. But she added: 'I find it terribly sad that each year on Pippa's birthday my memories are of operating theatres, drugs and a great many frightful, lonely, fearful hours.'

An Epidural Caesarean Birth

With her first birth Lynne had an emergency Caesarean section under general anaesthesia. The baby was born at 11.00 pm and she says she was 'so heavily drugged that I didn't wake until the next day and had little interest in the baby. No one thought to show him to me until midday.' She felt that in failing to give birth she had failed as a woman. The second time round she had an elective Caesarean section also with general anaesthesia and afterwards still felt, in her words, 'irrationally guilty'. The obstetrician advised her to be sterilized after that birth but she decided to go ahead and have another baby.

My third child, Amanda, was born eight months ago, and her birth was a very special one for me: it was my third Caesarean section and, thanks to the co-operation of the hospital staff, I was able to remain awake for the major part of the birth. The epidural that I was given numbed the lower half of my body, taking away the sensation of pain, but leaving enough feeling for me to know what was happening, and I was only put to sleep with a very light anaesthetic whilst I was being stitched up.

I first found out about epidural Caesareans on a television programme when I was 20 weeks pregnant, and asked at my next antenatal visit to the hospital if I could have one. Yes, if I still wanted to when the time came, and they saw no reason why not. I'm not sure whether I was pleased or sorry! I changed my mind several times in the next few weeks, but by the time I was 34 weeks pregnant I had found out all I could about epidurals, and was sure that I wanted it done.

In fact, the epidural itself (which was the only thing that I was scared of) was not as bad as I had imagined. The most surprising thing was the length of time it takes to put in place (about 10–15 minutes, plus another 10–15 minutes for it to start working) – a long time to lie on the operating table, wondering whether it would work. After a small pain-killing injection a metal tube is inserted into your backbone between two discs, and a fine plastic tube is pushed through the metal one. During this process you must lie *very* still, and a kind technician held my hand very tightly and talked about the weather throughout this 'ordeal', which really wasn't painful, but just strange – especially the thought of what was happening. Then came the wait, while everyone in the theatre stood and chatted and waited for me to go numb. After 8 minutes my thighs started to tingle – it was working, and I could hardly believe it. I felt as if everything was unreal and happening to someone else. Then the surgeon said 'I'm tired of waiting – give me a hypodermic.' My eyes opened wide as he proceeded to prod my abdomen, but I hardly felt a thing, it was as if he were tickling me lightly with a pinpoint.

At last it was really happening, and I could hardly wait, although it still felt as if I were watching someone else's operation. The surgeon started to cut, and I felt every inch of it, though without pain. I couldn't see his hands, as there was a green sheet draped over a frame in front of my head, but I knew all the time what was happening. I felt him put his hands inside my womb, stretching it as he got hold of the baby. I felt the pulling and stretching of my flesh as the baby's head came out; I strained my head to see over the sheet as I felt the arms and legs struggling to be free. I saw the surgeon's strong hands holding a pink body with a mop of wet dark hair – I already had two children, but had never before seen a newborn baby – and – it was a girl! After two sons, I had a daughter, and I had seen her born. I heard her first cry, I knew she was mine. Later, when I saw her wrapped in a blanket in her cot, I already loved her – I didn't have to learn, as I had with my sons.

Woman-to-Woman Support

There are many different forms of family and the pattern we think of as normal, a man and woman and their children, is only one. Increasingly single women are making the important decision to go ahead and have a child, and create a stable, loving home.

Kerry is a Lesbian mother with one child aged five. This is her description of the birth of her second baby.

I went to the British Pregnancy Advisory Service for artificial insemination because I couldn't find self-insemination and back up. I didn't know about this method before. I had to sleep with a man for Rowan [her son]. The father was very violent and I didn't stay with him. It was like a nightmare. I was very depressed – like a zombie. I didn't get out of that situation until Rowan was ten months old, when I escaped out of a window with him.

When Rowan was about two I read a book, *Rocking the Cradle*, about Lesbian mothers. It was a great relief. I hated sleeping with a man and didn't want to 'con' anybody.

Around that time I came out as a Lesbian. I was confiding in a friend what I was going to do and said, 'that doesn't mean I'm a Lesbian!' and we laughed it off. Later, it was something I realized I hadn't dared face. My aunt wrote and asked, 'Do you feel you may be a Lesbian?' When I read that I had a tremendous feeling of relief. During the pregnancy I went to a women's group and two of the women were very excited when I told them I was pregnant and asked if they could be at the birth.

I made a birth plan of things I wanted to happen or not to happen and went through it with my two friends. The first time I went to the hospital I took it with me and discussed it with the midwife who saw me. It didn't seem to irritate them at all. They were very good. I went in with qualms and came out happy.

On the day she was born I had taken Rowan to nursery school on my bike. I felt very good physically. I was building this very complex Lego castle for him, with 44 different stages. It was a challenge and I wanted to see if I could finish it before the baby came. I managed to by the time contractions got difficult. When they were four minutes apart we went to the hospital. I went on all fours on the back seat of the taxi, the only position that was comfortable, and Rowan and I collected Connie and Laura from a women's collective meeting. All the women came out on the street and waved us off. I gave them a grin and a thumbs up sign.

When I got out of the taxi contractions were coming strong and I crouched on the ground whilst I had another one. Then I paid the driver. We walked most of the way to the labour ward and then I crouched again. The labour ward was dimly lit with a beanbag on the floor and a thin mattress. It only took me an hour till the birth and the only point I came near feeling that it was all I could endure was when I was distracted by other people in the room.

The other annoying thing was when they wanted me to get up on to the bed for examination. That made it much more painful. It was hard to relax then. I'm sure they could have devised some method of examining me without having to do that.

It's difficult when you are in labour to be strong about everything. I had said if they went back on their word about Rowan being with me I would go out into the corridor and have her there. But it was as much as I could do to cope with the contractions, so I'm very glad that they accepted his being there as normal.

One nice thing was that I had some drawings of how Rowan imagined the birth and I blu-tacked them to the wall. Laura sat and held my hand. The contact was reassuring. Neither Laura nor Connie had been at a birth before. Their enthusiasm made up for that. They really shared the experience with me.

I had been going to antenatal yoga classes where I was taught to take my cues from my body. That was really helpful! I had meant to have my baby in the squatting position, but when it came to it that would have been too dramatic. Instead I was kneeling on all fours and leaning on my elbows. I'd gone into that position before when I had period pains. It was instinctive.

The second stage was lovely. There was no pain any longer. Unlike Rowan's birth, when I made no sound at all, with this birth I shouted. I turned round to Rowan and said, 'Don't worry! It's not hurting me! It just feels good to shout,' and he just nodded. He seemed very calm.

It felt a great relief to push – really satisfying. I could feel the baby moving bit by bit out of me. Suddenly she came with a rush and I could feel her head coming out, then her arms and legs and I could envisage the shape of her body as she came out. I felt dream-like. Connie was saying, 'Kerry, it's a girl!' I'd really not expected a girl. I'd *wanted* a girl but I hadn't allowed myself to think it could be.

Then I knelt straight upright and the placenta came out immediately. They wiped her face quickly. She didn't look at all messy. Then they handed her to me.

I had one little cut because she was coming out so fast. I'm only 5' 2" and she was 8 lb 12 oz, a chunky little thing. She was feeding within a half hour.

Then the celebration began. They all left the room and left us to it! Rowan started swinging off the lamp that comes down low over the bed. We all had something to eat and drink. After that I walked out and had a shower. It was lovely to be able to walk straight away.

She was born at three minutes past nine in the evening. Then they took us up to the isolation room because Connie was going to spend the night with Rowan and me. Rowan and I sat in the bed with the baby and we were wheeled up. It was great fun for him!

We all settled down for the night together, but I didn't sleep all night. I kept looking at her. It was lovely! Once I had fed her in the night I left her in bed with me. It seemed right.

When Rowan was born, in another hospital, they wheeled him away soon after the birth and I didn't see him for the whole night. I needed to be with him. I've learned now that the best course of action is to go with your feelings. And I would be more confident now. If they had taken her away I would have protested very firmly and insisted I stay with her, and maybe even decided to leave hospital with her.

I put in for a six-hour stay. In fact, I stayed longer because it was the middle of the night. Then we went back to champagne and later on that morning we all went round to the park and I sat in a swing with Kim (the baby) in a sling.

Born Before Arrival

This description is short – about as short as the labour, which lasted just over one hour. A precipitate labour like this can be shocking, not just because of pain, but because everything is going so fast that the woman may feel that she cannot catch up with what is happening inside her body.

When a birth occurs like this, before the midwife arrives, it is described as BBA – born before arrival.

From the moment my waters 'popped' I was in labour for one hour and ten minutes. It was incredibly intense – one contraction on top of the next, sometimes with hardly a pause for breath. I found myself on the floor of the bedroom on hands and knees, palms spread out downwards under my face saying loud *Ahhh*s throughout the entire labour. My husband sat on the bed to rub my back, running downstairs to open the door in preparation for the midwife, but before she could arrive my baby's head was already presenting. 'You'll have to push her out,' said my husband, trying to ease the polythene sheet under me. 'Who shall I phone?'

Suddenly I found myself in a wonderful powerful, dreamy, painfree place, and so open that our baby's head emerged effortlessly with no physical discomfort.

I took a deep breath and pushed, two more breaths and pushes and she was out. 'You're wonderful,' said my husband. And I turned over and embraced my daughter there on the floor in all the chaos. She made a few noises and fell asleep in my arms.

My two close friends Gill and Jackie (the general practitioner) arrived close on the heels of the midwife to find me sitting on my Woolworth's casserole dish waiting for the placenta and cuddling my daughter.

The relief doctor had lost his way and arrived as we were bathing baby. He stood for a minute respectfully and quietly and then set about checking over my lovely daughter. She weighed 9 lb and I hadn't felt her coming out!

My friends were wonderful, cleaning up, making tea and taking care of us all! It was the most triumphant and exciting day of my life!

An Active Birth

Active birth is one in which a woman is free to move around and change position right through the first and second stages of labour. She is not expected to adopt any positions for the convenience of her attendants but can choose those which give her the greatest comfort. Though a bed is in the room, she need not use it at all if she does not feel like it and can deliver on the floor, using a birth companion and any kind of furniture which gives her comfortable support.

This is an account of an active birth in which the woman kept moving and in which she was encouraged by her midwife to explore all the different positions in which she felt comfortable. Like many women in labour, Jenny found she wanted to make a noise and at times to make very powerful movements, and said that feeling free to do these things helped a great deal. Both she and her husband comment on the advantages of active birth compared with the more passive way in which she was expected to behave when her first baby was born.

On Wednesday I awoke with mild contractions early in the morning which then went off, recurring at breakfast time for about an hour. The remainder of the day was spent waiting for something to happen, but nothing did. The following morning, at my pre-arranged hospital appointment, the doctor told me I was 2 cm dilated. No more happened until two days later.

Early in the morning of Saturday I began to feel uncomfortable again and had five contractions between 2 and 3 am. By 5 am, when the contractions were coming at eight to ten minute intervals and lasting longer, we were on our way to the hospital. I felt I coped very well with the contractions as they were building up gradually and I was easily able to utilize my breathing control. During this time I was mainly sitting or standing.

Once at the hospital, the contractions died off for a while. I was told by the sister on duty that I would be checked regularly with the fetal trumpet as I wasn't going to have any other sort of monitor unless it was thought necessary. This I readily agreed to.

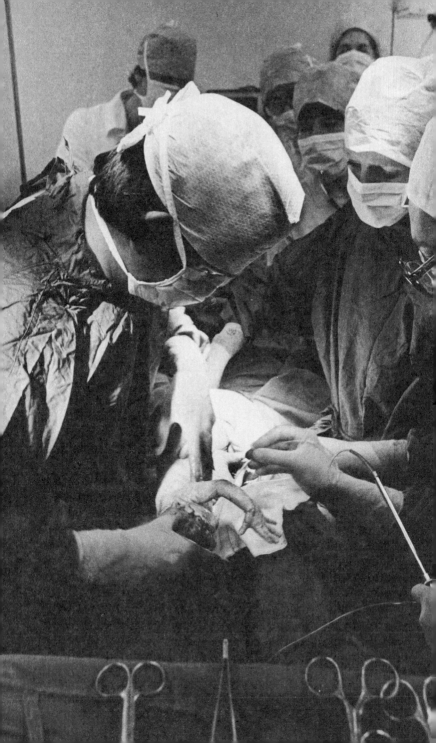

In the first-stage room the lighting was dim which made it more relaxing. Sister Thomas came in and told me to do exactly what I wanted – stand, sit, etc. I tried various positions for the contractions, now every three minutes or so. I stood leaning over the bed on my elbows; I leant on my husband; I leant on the wall – leaning forwards; and lay on the bed on my side and occasionally on my back. We were in the first-stage room for only half an hour. My breathing control helped me to cope with the contractions well.

I was given several drinks of iced water all through labour and afterwards – a very welcome surprise.

I was then told I could go through to the delivery room which was dimly lit by one spotlight. The usual delivery bed was in its place but to the left of this was a mattress on the floor, covered in sheeting. At the foot of the mattress was a chair.

I tried various positions – standing, leaning on my husband, lying on my side, mainly kneeling. Squatting on my toes was not very comfortable. My legs felt weak and I didn't use the frame which was provided at all. I could not have delivered in the standing, leaning back position as Michel Odent prefers, because of the weakness of my legs. The most comfortable position I found was kneeling forwards with my arms resting on two pillows on the chair; at least I found it comfortable until the chair moved in the middle of a contraction and took me with it! It was swiftly moved then so that it was against the wall at the head end of the mattress. Between contractions I sat back on to my feet to relax.

Soon afterwards I reached transition, during which I was sick again, kept going cold and wanting to be covered up with a sheet and had intermittent bouts of shaking which I could only control by concentration on my breathing. I banged on the floor hard with my feet during this stage – I don't know why but somehow it helped! All of this only lasted about 10 to 15 minutes but I was very pleased when it stopped and I was able to begin pushing.

I had been offered Entonox earlier but was told by the sister that she didn't think I would need it, which I didn't. Throughout, I was given every encouragement to move as and when I wanted.

I knelt, supported by the chair, throughout the second stage and although I had forgotten how strong the pain was I found I could push a lot harder as I was pushing against the solid floor. My husband was sitting next to me between the mattress and the delivery bed and I was able to hold on to his hands and arms and concentrate on pushing. I had only been pushing for about 20 minutes when Sister Thomas (herself kneeling low on the mattress) told me to feel down, and I was surprised to find that Andrew's head was already born – I didn't realize at all. Then there were only a couple more contractions before he was born.

I had only a slight tear with just a small amount of stitching. I have been very pleased at the speed at which I have healed and how little discomfort I have had – even while I was in hospital!

Andrew was immediately given to my husband to hold whilst I was being manoeuvred into a semi-sitting position for the third stage. This was rather awkward. I had no injections for this and only two or three contractions saw the delivery of the placenta. I then held him and he went straight to the breast.

Some of the advantages felt by my husband

My husband compared his role in this birth and the first one and concluded that he had felt far more important this time. He was able to be more physically supportive. By my being more mobile so was he, and the support was much closer, more personal than just holding my hand and wiping my face. It was much more satisfying for him.

Some of the advantages I felt

I found a lot of advantages in giving birth this way. How much of it is due to it being my second time and how much to mobility and position cannot be ascertained. However, this way was definitely preferred.

Firstly, I was very impressed with the quality of the care I was given and felt that I was treated with a lot of respect.

I felt much more in control, as if I knew what I was doing.

The contractions were much easier to cope with, despite the sickness, shaking and feeling faint, because of the gradual build-up. I enjoyed the freedom of movement, being able to position myself for relief and rarely lying on my back, and kneeling leaning forward seemed to relieve the pressure and give me less back discomfort.

Pushing in the second stage seemed much easier. The solid base of the floor made it easier to push hard – much easier than pushing against the midwife – and I am convinced that gravity helped also.

The fact that I had only a small tear may or may not have been due to position but was a distinct advantage. I felt very comfortable knowing that pain relief was at hand if I should require it and would not have been happy to commit myself to non-use from the outset (as M. Odent prefers).

I found this birth a very satisfying and unique experience, not just because of the arrival of our son, but because I was made to feel special. I felt in control most of the time and always directly involved in all the proceedings.

On the Move in a High-Tech Hospital

A written birth plan can help a woman make certain that she has the kind of help she wants from those caring for her. It is important that it is flexible so that if labour is different from how she expects it to be she can make decisions at the time and does not feel that she has been 'programmed' in advance.

Here the woman describes exactly what she wants, makes two concessions to hospital policy in agreeing to have an external fetal monitor for short periods and to artificial rupture of the membranes at 7 cm – about the time when in many labours membranes rupture spontaneously anyway – but otherwise does exactly what she wants and keeps moving around.

A change of shift means that she feels uncared for at a vital phase of her labour, the transition between the first and the second stages, and she holds on and tries not to push in an effort to prevent the cervix swelling when the baby's head is being pressed against it before it is fully opened. That kind of desperate struggle to avoid pushing is probably unnecessary. If you have to push you have to push! It would have been easier for her if she had continued to breathe lightly for as long as she was able and then just did the minimum push, allowing herself to feel open, when the urge was irresistible.

She has a lovely, enjoyable second stage, with her midwives lying on the floor beside her and giving gentle reassurance and praise.

All this happens in a hospital which is not used to this kind of birth but, because the staff are listening to what women want, is able to adapt to new (yet actually age-old) ways of birthing.

I enjoyed the labour much more than I expected to. I discussed the type of birth that I hoped for with one of the doctors (I never saw 'my' consultant) and typed out my wishes on a 'Birth Plan' which was attached to my notes. I wanted a natural birth with as little interference as possible. This was my main worry, as the consultant in charge was known to favour a mechanized birth.

I was admitted to hospital two days after my EDD (estimated date of delivery) as I was found to have high blood pressure at the clinic. Several other patients were admitted on that day and I was the only one not to be induced, as I had specifically asked not to be unless absolutely necessary. I was sent home after two days and began labour the next day. I waited until my contractions were every five minutes until going to hospital – I had then been in regular labour for about six hours. I was only 2 cm dilated at this stage, so I was left in a small labour room with my husband. I had requested no enema or shaving. I was also anxious not to have an internal fetal monitor which is normally attached to all women. I agreed to have short periods with an external (belt) monitor if considered necessary. I subsequently had this attached for three 20-minute periods. This was quite uncomfortable, especially during transition.

I was assigned a student midwife who popped in now and again and admitted that she knew nothing about types of breathing, so I was glad that I had my husband with me! The midwife offered advice when I began to experience pain and although she offered drugs for pain relief I did not feel pressurized. She also made suggestions *re* psychoprophylaxis which proved helpful. I was admitted to hospital at 10 pm and by 5 am I was 7 cm dilated but beginning to feel tired. Although I was originally opposed to the idea of an amniotomy (artificial rupture of the membranes) I agreed to have one at this time as I was told it would speed things up and was moved to the delivery room for this operation. It was the first time I actually lay down, as I had previously sat on the bed with my feet on a chair or walked up and down the labour room. I found lying down much more uncomfortable.

Things began to speed up after my waters were broken and I was soon fully dilated. My contractions were almost continuous by this time, and quite painful. Unfortunately, this was the time when there was a change in shifts and a new midwife and student midwife came on.

For some time I had an anterior lip and was virtually hanging off the delivery table in an effort not to push. The midwife examined me and told me I could begin pushing and I did wonder whether I could have begun earlier, as no one had examined me for some time.

I was asked which position I wished to deliver in and said I would prefer to be on the floor. The mattress and some sheets were laid on the floor and I can honestly say that I thoroughly enjoyed the rest of the birth. I tried various positions but found sitting upright in front of my husband most comfortable. The nurse and midwife were super and explained everything. They thought nothing of lying on the floor with a fetal trumpet. There was no urging to push harder, only praise and gentle encouragement, and although this stage lasted two hours, I found it exhilarating rather than tiring. The cord was cut as soon as Emma's head was delivered, as it was wrapped around her neck.

I had asked not to have an episiotomy and had a small tear. I think this was partly due to my over-strenuous pushing, and because I was not told to pant until the very last minute. I also asked not to have an injection to expel the afterbirth.

She was born at twelve minutes past nine and I put her straight to the breast before we were 'cleaned up'. I was stitched and given the usual cup of tea. It was a further two and a half hours before I was back on the ward and I was glad that everything seemed so unhurried.

I have become something of a celebrity as it is unusual to have a 'natural' birth in this hospital.

A Matter for Complaint

What do you do when the experience of childbirth has been marred by inadequate care, insensitivity and rigidly applied rules which do not take into account *your* needs and wishes? Here a woman describes a labour which was a mixture of good and bad things. She met individuals who respected her wishes and treated her as a person, but the system allowed for no continuity of care and there was poor communication between different members of staff. Everything depended on who was on duty at the time. The woman was merely at the receiving end of care and was expected to be a passive patient. She tells what she did about it and says the experience taught her to be assertive.

My waters broke when I was having lunch with friends, two weeks before my estimated date of delivery. When I rang the hospital I was advised to go to the nearest hospital for an examination. My husband, Thomas, was very relieved when they said I was only 2 cm dilated and would definitely make it back to London. We were able to drive straight to the hospital and were soon settled in our delivery room. By this time I was starting to feel gentle, irregular contractions, but nothing much showed up on the monitor, so Thomas went home, changed and had a bath and came back armed with coffee, sandwiches and all the Sunday papers ready for a long night's vigil. I was in no pain, very excited and really looking forward to sharing the next few hours with him.

No sooner had he settled down with me, however, than the midwife on duty came in and announced that she was moving me to an antenatal ward where I could get some sleep, as things seemed to be moving so slowly, and that Thomas could go home. He wanted to protest, but I thought she must have good reasons for her decision and wouldn't let him, although I knew that I could sleep quite well where I was if I wanted to and that he would be so afraid of not hearing the phone summoning him to return that he wouldn't sleep properly at home.

It was just after midnight when Thomas and a student midwife settled me into an antenatal bed and left me. Three or

four long-term patients were gathered round one bed with a TV showing a late film which didn't stop until 1 am. They were gossiping like schoolgirls until long after that, mostly about ghastly deliveries they had heard of and incompetent medical staff. It was quite impossible for me to sleep and when my contractions suddenly got much stronger I couldn't concentrate on my relaxation.

Eventually the midwife told the other girls to settle down, but by this time my contractions were coming thick and fast. I tried to time them but in the dark and without my glasses it was very difficult. I didn't know how to get myself back to the delivery room or when I should ask to be transferred. When I thought my contractions were coming every five to seven minutes I went out to ask the night staff nurse if I could be moved. Her reply was that I should go on a monitor first, and although there was one already by my bed in the delivery room she insisted on my staying where I was while she tried three other machines before getting one to work. The verdict was that I was not yet ready to move. Only when my student midwife came to see how I was did I manage to get transferred and we had to run the gauntlet of the staff nurse, who tried to protest that as I had contaminated the sheets in her ward I must stay there! This was about 5 am and from then on my labour was conducted exactly as I wanted, with the support of two wonderful student midwives, until the point where the baby showed signs of distress and had to be whipped out with forceps.

It was not so satisfactory for my husband as it might have been, however, because although I left it as late as possible before asking for him to be contacted he felt far worse after a restless night's sleep than he would have done with none, and he arrived into the middle of a situation which he should have been part of throughout. It was much harder for him to find me in pain than it would have been if he'd seen it build up and been able to help me through the early stages.

The delivery room was comfortable – with dimmed lights. I could move around, go for walks and have a bath when not being monitored. Thomas was never excluded. The senior midwives were calm and reassuring, my permission was asked for every examination and when the baby's heart showed signs

The belt around this woman's abdomen is the external monitor which records the fetal heartbeat.

of stress after a prolonged second stage everything was done with my understanding and consent in the course of a difficult forceps delivery. The baby had to be taken straight to the special care baby unit. My husband was able to see him three hours after birth and was given two photos to take back to me. The paediatrician came back to the delivery room to explain to me what had gone wrong and how they would deal with the problems as soon as he'd settled the baby in. The difficulty was that there was no liaison between staff on the special care baby unit and those on the postnatal ward and it was difficult for me to see my baby as often as I would have liked because the special care baby unit is downstairs, the lift was often out of action and it entailed a long walk down corridors when I was in pain from stitches. There is not enough space in the special care baby unit. Parents can visit at any time but feel in the way near so many ill babies. It was very uncomfortable for me to try to breastfeed because the staff there had no time to help and did not understand that I was in pain from stitches.

Postnatal care varied greatly according to the staff duty. I had the least considerate staff in the early days when I felt most vulnerable. They gave quite a lot of help to nursing mothers but tended to glance at the empty cot by my bed, say 'Oh, you haven't got a baby' and pass on, instead of asking if I was worried about my baby being in special care. There was no information about ward routine so one never knew when to expect meals. Other patients told me about 6 am–tea outside the ward, which they had discovered by accident after three days. The food was poor, the last meal was at 5.30 pm and the last hot drink at 8 pm. Orderlies put food on a central table and those only just up from delivery or with Caesareans had to rely on other patients to bring theirs to them. There were plenty of bidets and baths but several of the bidets were out of order during the whole of my stay.

The night staff were unsympathetic and treated the patients very harshly. When I asked for help changing my sanitary towels at 2 am on my first night I was told, 'They're in your locker – get them yourself.'

On my third day a wonderful midwife came on duty who really took trouble in assessing each woman's state of health and mind and made me feel for the first time that somebody really cared. Too many nurses say breezily, 'How are you?' expecting the answer 'fine', so that is the answer one tends to give.

There is a sequel to this tale of woe. I talked about it to various acquaintances who are nurses and to the midwife when I took my baby Alexander along to an antenatal class reunion. They all said that I should complain to the hospital about what had happened so that the authorities would know what was going on. So I wrote to the head of midwifery services at the hospital and received a very prompt reply, apologizing for the unsatisfactory treatment I'd received and asking if she could come to see me to discuss the matter further. This she did, along with a hospital administrator, and they both expressed distress that members of their staff should have acted contrary to the hospital's philosophy of maternity and general nursing care. The sister who transferred me to the antenatal ward was guilty in their view of insensitivity in making a decision for me instead of giving me a choice. There were only two of us in labour so there was no pressure on delivery rooms and we could certainly have stayed where we were, but the sister had felt that as we were progressing slowly we would need some sleep. She obviously didn't realize we wouldn't get it on the antenatal ward.

I cannot really blame her as I did not protest at the time, but I have learnt from my experience to be more assertive in the future and she has apparently been told not to be patronizing and to be more aware of the needs of different patients. The antenatal staff nurse, however, and one on the postnatal ward, about whom I also complained, are known to be hostile to patients and I gather they will be disciplined.

I was very impressed by the speed and thoroughness with which my complaint got investigated. The administrative staff seemed pleased to have feedback from a patient and I was able to make some positive points and constructive suggestions as well, so that I am really looking forward to having another baby there some day when I will feel better able to cope with the experience.

I cannot emphasize enough, however, the need to state one's

wishes. Even in a hospital like this one, where the philosophy seems right, there are always individuals to whom it has not filtered through. Until I went into hospital I felt that many women started off with a negative attitude to the staff and that the last thing I wanted was to adopt an aggressive approach and be labelled as 'difficult'. Now I know that tactful firmness in expressing one's feelings is essential, however difficult that may be in the middle of labour!

A Slow Second Labour

Every labour is different. When you are having a second baby it is important not to anticipate a labour which is a repetition of the first one. Though most second labours are shorter than the first – often only about half as long – they may turn out to be longer. This does not mean that there is anything wrong.

A slow labour in a woman who has already had babies is often treated as abnormal, however. Here a woman having a home birth describes a labour like this, following a previous labour which was all over in three hours.

It was a very strange twelve hours. I had had a false alarm two days before, but after the midwife called, everything stopped. I knew she was going on holiday at the end of the week. I felt in my bones that everything was ready. Then contractions started and we decided to ring the midwife again. In the early hours of the morning she arrived with a pupil and informed me that I was 6 cm dilated. My last child had arrived in three hours so we were hopeful. Things, however, seemed to be going slower this time but I was very relaxed and comfortable and not worried at all. I stood warming my rear at the wood stove discussing bread-making as my guests ate vast quantities of my home-made bread and drank tea. Morning broke, it was a beautiful crisp sunny day for a change, but I was still 6 cm – disappointing.

At one point during the morning I went into the bathroom, sat on the loo and found I was very comfortable in that position. It was so funny – in came the midwife, the pupil and my husband with a rug for my knees, and I sat, for an hour, as the three 'brass monkeys' sat on the side of the bath.

I had now been in labour for 12 hours and was feeling relaxed and in control, even sleeping briefly between contractions. This ability to doze off was worrying the midwife who was not used to NCT breathing and my husband had to reassure her I was not exhausted, just very calm. I then heard discussions about 'taking me in' if things didn't move faster. I was worried about this as I was still mobile and very much in command of my body. I did not need medication and the baby was not in distress. At this stage my GP arrived and when he saw I was still only 6 cm he decided to break my waters. I was against this at first but he explained that it appeared the head was not pressing against the cervix evenly and allowing the anterior lip to draw up. He hoped that by rupturing the membranes the pressure would even out and allow labour to progress. I accepted this, as he supported my wish not to have pethidine or be moved. I heard the waters pour over the floor, thanking God we had bare, stained boards and rugs rather than carpets.

Things happened rapidly after that. 3 am! A strong contraction followed rapidly by an urge to push. I was examined by the midwife who ran in from the kitchen, thinking she'd have time for lunch, and told me, 'Don't push yet.' I had expected a transitional phase because of the delayed dilatation and I got one, with a vengeance. My husband said it was only five minutes but it seemed forever. Then I pushed with everything I'd saved up and the head arrived, one more push and my son slid out, with an Apgar level of nine, into the sunshine.

Champagne followed, and congratulations. The midwives were impressed by the NCT training.

The worst thing about a home birth was the amount of washing to do the next day and the fact that I was up milking the goat by the next evening as she refused to let down for anyone else.

Now eight and a half months, my son, once an unplanned and unwanted fetus, is the centre of the family and beautiful!

Overall, the experience which I dreaded has been one of the most enriching of my life, in every respect.

A Sixth Baby

It might be expected that anyone having her sixth baby would be fairly confident about childbirth. But for a woman who is professionally involved in maternity care there can be great anxiety because being a 'grand multipara' is considered risky and almost to be courting danger. A woman who is labelled 'high risk' may have an easy, straightforward birth. Many women nowadays are conditioned to expect excessive pain or a great deal of obstetric intervention simply because they are older mothers, first-time mothers, have had previous miscarriages or a stillbirth, already have a large family, or have gone past the estimated date of delivery.

Here is an account of a home birth in New York by a woman who is a childbirth teacher and breastfeeding counsellor. She reveals how naturally birth can take place at home surrounded by members of the family. She also describes what an exciting experience it can be for the other children.

At 38 I really was emotionally insecure this time, thanks to so much emphasis on 'high risk' at the numerous conferences I've attended. I was eight days 'over' the due date and went to bed Saturday night at 2 am after finishing the laundry. I wakened at 7 am and was excited because I had had a show – lovely! I felt early contractions and held a class for seven couples in my home. Then I did a bit of cleaning and read the Sunday papers for the rest of the day. In the evening I was reading *The Complete Book of Pregnancy and Childbirth** which I had vowed to finish before I had the baby. At 10.40 pm I was up to the glossary and literally had finished reading the very last word about amniotomy when POP! I couldn't believe the coincidence.

I called the doctor and woke up my husband. At 11.15 pm the doctor arrived. I was walking around, automatically doing my breathing. Two of the children were taking pictures. We had a tape recorder going. Later I laughed at my thoughts of ensuring a quiet atmosphere. Right through this labour, excitement and joy, the mixed emotions during expulsion, and

* UK edition entitled *Pregnancy & Childbirth*, Sheila Kitzinger (Penguin, 1986).

encouragement from everyone, created constant noise.

At 12.05 am I got on the bed on all fours. I think this is a psychologically comforting position. My head was against the headboard pillows. Three pushes, carefully controlled, and then Stephen slid out. Pictures reveal my three and a half year old on the bed the entire time looking fascinated, and at one point with his arms around me. 'You are all right Mummy,' he said.

In the excitement after the initial cry, I found myself embarrassed but proud when my ten and a half year old son said, 'Ma, shouldn't you be putting him to the breast now?' Of course!

Then everyone went to bed and Stephen and I were a nursing couple for two hours straight. We rested all day.

At 7 pm that evening we took the baby to the paediatrician. At 8 pm my husband, the baby and I went to Brooklyn where I had a childbirth class for a new group. The baby slept. I felt great!

Facing up to Fear

A bad birth experience which has been pushed into the background of a woman's mind, or which is dismissed by others as being unimportant compared with the job of having a healthy baby, can cast a long shadow forward into the next pregnancy. Feelings of powerlessness and being out of control – of being trapped and helpless – flood in afresh as the approaching birth draws near. Unless she takes time to face up to her fears and is able to talk about them with someone who understands – and who accepts her emotions and does not try to change them – a pregnant woman may be overwhelmed by fear. A positive approach to childbirth and effective coping strategies need to be built on to the self-confidence which comes from acknowledging and confronting anxiety.

Here is the story of a courageous woman who never revealed just how awful her first birth had been. She vomited right the way through and wanted to die so that it would finish.

When I was eight months pregnant with my second child I faced a crisis about the impending labour.

I had approached my first pregnancy and labour with great excitement and enthusiasm. I exercised regularly, ate well, practised my breathing techniques religiously, and read everything I could on the subject of childbirth. I was really looking forward to the experience.

I knew labour would be painful, and I had a clear idea about the type of pain relief I'd want if needed – but I'd hoped I wouldn't need it. I felt well prepared. I thought I could conquer the pains and control the experience. Whatever fear I had remained largely unacknowledged.

As it turned out, my 12-hour labour was accompanied by the very unusual experience of vomiting with every contraction. I eventually had an epidural – for which I was very thankful – but Justin had to be delivered by forceps, and that was disappointing. However, I was so thrilled to have a healthy baby son I quickly put the awfulness of the labour behind me.

And there it remained until my second labour loomed on the horizon. Eight weeks before my daughter was born I was seized with a vivid and frightening 're-experience' of my first labour. I actually feared another because the first had been so awful. And yet part of me wanted to give birth again, just to prove to myself that I could 'do it right this time'. I felt my body had let me down before, and I desperately didn't want that to happen again.

One night when I returned from my NCT class in tears, I confessed to my husband that I was worried that this time would be like the last. At first he was very reassuring, saying, 'Of course it won't be, it will be much easier.' But these reassurances seemed to me a denial of my experience. I'd expected it to be grand then and look what had happened. This time I'd decided to be prepared for the worst. I felt I'd lost control then and couldn't cope. This time I *had* to cope.

Then my husband said something which really rang a bell. 'You women and all this natural childbirth business. It's become the female version of machismo. There's all this pressure on you to prove your womanhood, to show you can bear up to the pain of childbirth. It's a load of nonsense.' His words rang true. I had to prove something to myself, and in some subtle way I couldn't define, to my female friends as well.

There was some test going on here. After menstruation, childbirth is the great rite of passage for a woman, one's initiation into motherhood, a kind of trial by fire. And how we 'managed' it said something both to others and, more importantly, to ourselves. Part of me felt competitive about it: 'If she could do without pain relief so could I'. I'd even heard a woman once apologize for needing pain relief.

Facing my second go at this rite of passage I was both less self-confident and more determined. I openly acknowledged that I was afraid, not so much of the pain, but of losing control over my body. My vomiting had been a loss of control and the rest of the experience had been dominated by it up until my son was actually born. And then nothing mattered to me but that we were both all right.

But now I felt anxious that my body would once again not perform as it should (or rather as I thought it should – there's certainly no law against vomiting your way through labour!).

During one particularly emotional day I telephoned Sheila

[Kitzinger], who kindly said come round and talk. It wasn't long into the conversation before I was re-living the feelings I'd had during the first labour: my stomach hurt and I felt breathless and fearful. I was soon in tears, confessing the great disappointment I'd felt in my body. It seemed very important that I re-live all these feelings in order to integrate them, and that this 're-experiencing' would help to dissipate the emotional blockage I felt towards another labour. I wanted to approach this new one afresh. Acknowledging these feelings helped me a great deal and over the next few days I began to look forward to the new birth. I felt I had broken through this fear and anxiety in order to accept that whatever happened was all right – what would be would be. I would surrender to the labour and let my body do whatever it needed to get through.

As it turned out the birth of my daughter was like my fantasy labour – short, sweet and without complications – far better than I'd dared to hope: I had a perfect Christmas Day. The morning was spent leisurely helping Justin (three and three months) open his presents – a new bike and train set. In the afternoon we went next door for a superb traditional Christmas lunch. Then we took a walk, saw some more neighbours and joked that the baby wasn't coming today. (I was already a week overdue.)

But at 9 pm, when I took Justin upstairs to bed and read him a story, I found I was having to read while timing my contractions! – every ten minutes, no, every eight, no six! In half an hour they went from nine to four minutes apart. They felt like very sharp period pains, and although they were coming closer and closer together I'd prepared myself for a longish labour so I was quite relaxed about them. I came downstairs, sent Robert up to sing the required rounds of 'Pussy Cat, Pussy Cat, where have you been?' and when he returned I crossed my fingers. His face brightened. 'Something's happening?' He was excited.

I asked him to bring the straight-backed chair downstairs and to lend me his watch with the second hand on it. I went to the bathroom. I was getting hot and cold flushes and I had 'the runs'. I thought for a moment that I might have a tummy bug, and the severe cramping was just part of it, as the pains were coming every one and a half to two minutes.

Robert popped next door and put Amanda, who was to come and babysit for us, on alert. I had planned to have a long, leisurely bath – one of the many things on my list of time-consuming and relaxing things to do at home while in labour. But there wasn't enough hot water. A fortuitous thing it proved to be.

Robert popped his head round the bathroom door just as I was throwing up my Christmas dinner. 'Now I know I'm in labour,' I joked. He said we'd better get my things packed – a week overdue and I hadn't packed my suitcase yet! (Another of my staying-at-home chores.) He phoned the hospital and Amanda, who arrived ten minutes later. It was 10.15 pm. I asked her to make some sandwiches and put some food in a bag, while I stood leaning against the kitchen dresser breathing heavily through each contraction. They were very close together and still I hadn't a clue.

Meanwhile Robert, who had furiously raced around the house getting my things together, had the car warmed up and ready to go and was telling me to get in. I was quite happy to stay put, and I asked Amanda to read off the 'list of things to take with you' from Sheila Kitzinger's book. At 10.30 pm Robert literally dragged me to the car. He, at least, had a sense of urgency.

In the car I knelt on the passenger seat and held on to the neck rest. Thank God for it! The contractions were so intense I started to hallucinate. I kept seeing red and orange patterns around my field of vision. Robert gave a running commentary as to where we were on the journey. As we pulled up to the hospital I was making a fair amount of noise and he was temporarily confused and pulled up to the wrong entrance. When I saw the hospital lights the pains were so intense I thought, 'If they tell me I'm three centimetres I'll beg them for anything!' By the time Robert wheeled the car around to the right entrance I wanted to push!

I felt my waters break and the baby's head moving down. I got out of the car and had another contraction as Robert rushed about getting bags and my suitcase. We took the long blue walk through the huge hallway with me panting away. It was just after 11 pm.

We rushed into the admission room. Robert pulled off the bottom of my tracksuit. I cried out to the midwife, 'I want to push,' and climbed on to the bed. I'd already decided to remain as upright as possible, so I knelt with my back to the foot of the bed and held on to the metal headboard. I was panting and screaming through another contraction while the midwife examined me. She confirmed what I already knew – I could push.

They wheeled the bed through the corridor into a delivery suite. I was making a fair racket but I didn't care. It seemed the most natural thing in the world to make the noises I was making. Mind you, I could hardly hear the midwife's instructions. I was completely absorbed in the rush of sensations. Overwhelmed by pains that felt wonderful. My endorphins* must have been at full tilt.

Robert stood beside me and held my forehead with one hand, the other on my still fully-clothed back. Someone was trying to put a monitor on my abdomen to get a heartbeat, but couldn't. Evelyn, the midwife, told me to push into my bottom. I felt a pain and she told me to wait and not push with the next contraction. So much pain I couldn't tell what was happening. Again I pushed, and this time the head came through. Another giant push and out she squirted! It was 11.34 pm.

I turned and looked down over my shoulder and saw my daughter squirming, wet, bloody, quietly gulping in her first breaths. The midwife wiped her face and mouth. Someone put a blanket round her. I lay back on the foot of the bed and a few minutes later, with no trouble, out came the placenta. It was a lovely, speckled, purple-brownish blob.

Then they put the baby on my chest. Robert and I smiled at her crinkled little face. 'What are you going to call her?' Evelyn asked. Robert suggested Rachel. I said 'Christina,' and we both agreed. I hadn't even thought about that name before.

I got the shakes and I shook for an hour! Evelyn told me she had had to cut me – I didn't even know. I didn't remember the sequence of things so I asked her to review what had happened. While I had my feet in the stirrups so they could stitch me up (I had three internal and five external stitches, a good second

* see Glossary

degree tear!) I had the midwife bring a mirror to show me the stitches. She thought this a little funny, but I congratulated her on her needlework. I was shaking so badly I couldn't keep my legs open. I asked for a sherry. It being Christmas someone actually brought both me and Robert one. Later someone came to 'present' Christina with a few little gifts, something for each baby born on Christmas Day.

She weighed 7 lb 3 oz. I felt really chuffed, especially after all the scanning they'd done, and all the feeling around. I had been told I had a 'delicate' baby – 6, not more than 6½lb – I showed them!

I felt a wonderful sense of elation and achievement. And I felt triumphant. I had done it! Virtually with ease. The birth had been a catharsis for my experience with Justin. Robert and I both felt enormously pleased and contented. A healthy baby girl, what more could we want?

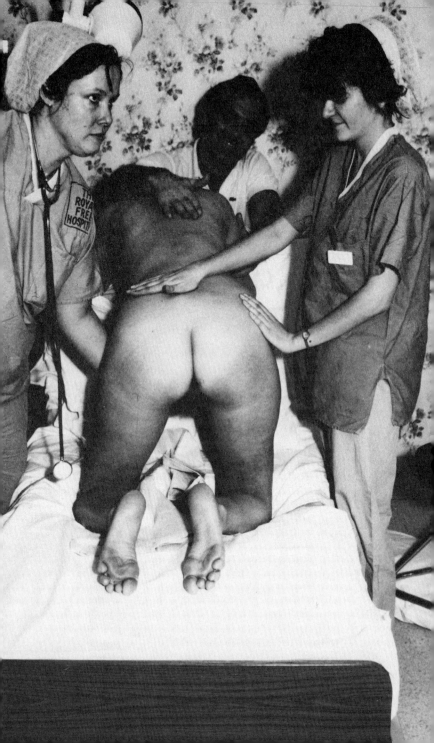

Vaginal Birth after Two Caesarean Sections

It is often not realized how strong a woman's sense of failure may be after a Caesarean birth and how she may long to be able to give birth naturally next time. In the USA doctors often say, 'Once a Caesarean always a Caesarean.' This is not so in Europe, where Caesarean section rates are much lower, and unless the same conditions are present in the subsequent labour, obstetricians plan for a vaginal delivery. In this account a woman describes how she felt after two Caesarean deliveries, her determination to have a vaginal birth if she possible could, and her triumphal achievement with the birth of her third baby.

We have now had our third son, Alan, born vaginally after what turned out to be quite an easy labour – and what a wonderful experience it was! I'm feeling on top of the world.

After my second Caesarean I tried to accept the fact that I would never give birth normally, but I just couldn't. I felt like an outsider, envious of other mothers. Whenever one of my friends had a happy normal delivery I would try to be pleased for her but it always made me even more disappointed at what I had missed. I began to read as much as I could about it and found that it had been done in America and that a few obstetricians advocated it in this country, although I couldn't find any actual cases. I became desperate to be allowed to try.

I had been to see my consultant before I embarked on this pregnancy to see if I would be allowed a 'trial of labour' and he agreed that, providing things looked favourable, he would let me, although he wasn't very optimistic about my chances. He was taking a risk by allowing this, particularly in view of the Wendy Savage case, because it is very much against hospital policy and he said he would have to be personally responsible for me.

My pregnancy was uneventful and I felt fit and well. The problem with my first two deliveries had been fetal distress because both babies had their cords wrapped several times around their necks and there was also a slight doubt about my pelvis as they had both been posterior with high, free heads and I had gone very overdue both times.

Towards the end of my pregnancy I began to wonder whether I was doing the right thing or if I really was putting my life and my baby's life at risk. I became obsessed with maternal and perinatal mortality statistics! However I tried to think positively and have faith.

The consultant thought it would be best to induce me on my due date to try and ensure the baby would be in the best possible condition. He used Prostin pessaries which worked wonderfully. There was no question of having an enema or a shave, or my husband wearing a silly hat and gown. I only had three periods of continuous monitoring after the pessaries were administered and the rest of the time I was discouraged from lying on the bed and actively encouraged to walk about, take baths and adopt different positions. At one stage we discussed the pros and cons of breaking my waters and I decided I would rather not, which was accepted happily. Everything was very informal, relaxed and friendly and this all made me feel that it was my labour and that I was in control, with friendly staff there to help me if I needed it.

I had three Prostin pessaries, starting in the morning and then at three hourly intervals, and by mid-afternoon I was in good, normal labour with none of the disadvantages of a drip and ARM. Labour progressed rapidly – I was 3–4 cm at 6.00 pm and fully dilated at 7.30 pm.

When I was in labour I didn't really think about the scars at all, I was so taken up by the whole experience. I was very happy with the way the labour went. Although I was induced, the Prostin pessaries seemed to be a very natural method of induction and I think if they were available at the chemist a lot of women would use them! I thought I would have to be monitored very closely but in fact this was not the case and I had a very active labour which I'm sure helped me both physically and mentally. The only part of the labour I found difficult was the last three-quarters to an hour of the first stage and this must have been transition because although I had only been about 3–4 cm half an hour before this, the contractions suddenly became overwhelming and I was getting the urge to bear down. I felt very confused because people were telling me I had another two to three hours to go! I felt very upset at this stage too – as though I could have had a good cry. I was surprised at how intense and powerful all the sensations were – my body was completely taken over by them. This was in total contrast to the Caesareans when I didn't feel involved at all – I was just a bystander, helpless on an operating table. I pushed for about half an hour and then, as I was bleeding a bit and the baby's heartbeat was dropping, he was lifted out easily in one push with forceps. It turned out that my scar was fine and the bleeding was from some vulval varicose veins.

Although I had been pleased when my last baby was delivered it was nothing like the emotion I felt when Alan was born. I shouted: 'I did it!' as I reached forward to lift his body out of mine and I felt totally satisfied, fulfilled, incredibly happy and at peace with myself again. Words can't describe that moment, when I think of it now I feel that same emotion. I didn't mind forceps at all – mainly because of the way the rest of the labour went and the attitude of the staff at St James. Things have changed an awful lot since I had my first baby there four and a half years ago. The staff treated me as a guest rather than as a patient and couldn't do enough for me. The other thing is that I can finally lay to rest my feelings about the Caesareans and accept them as being necessary to save my babies' lives. Now I feel 'normal', at one with other women and mothers who have shared the same experience. When I think that I could so easily have had a third section if I hadn't made a fuss it makes me shudder. I can't explain how it feels emotionally to have a Caesarean, even when you know it's necessary, because it's so tied up with one's psychological, emotional and sexual life and with one's self-image as a woman. All I know is that if I hadn't achieved a normal delivery and felt my body working as it should do I would have always regretted it and it would have been one of the biggest disappointments of my life. I know that sounds silly and selfish when the result was a healthy baby – but it's not a logical feeling and I know a lot of other women feel the same way. Everything possible should be done to avoid unnecessary Caesareans. A lot more should be done to help women who have had Caesareans, both physically and emotionally, through sympathetic understanding and counselling.

Three Days, Two Nights

Here is a description of a long labour of which only the latter part was spent in hospital. Care was given by a community midwife.

This is the kind of birth which under consultant care usually entails a great deal of intervention throughout, simply because everything is taking so long. Because dilatation of the cervix does not take place according to an established norm the uterus is often stimulated with oxytocin through an intravenous drip from the moment when it is decided that there are deviations from the normal. As it was, the midwife, who knew the woman wanted as natural a birth as possible, managed to hold off all intervention until the evening of the second day. At this point Rosie's cervix was fully dilated and there was a pause in labour – something which often happens before the onset of the active second stage if the baby's head is not yet deeply descended in the pelvis. Doctors and midwives are usually concerned that the uterus has ceased working, a diagnosis of secondary uterine inertia is made and the decision is taken to stimulate uterine activity artificially. That is what happened in this case.

Another view of the situation is that the uterus, and the mother, needed a rest at this phase and that if everyone had waited patiently and had allowed her to relax, contractions would have picked up again and the baby might have been delivered without all the fuss – and the distress it caused the woman – which resulted from a forced expulsive stage.

The actual birth was beautiful, with the community midwife again shepherding the mother through the experience, resisting instructions from a junior doctor to do an episiotomy, and the mother and midwife working together to achieve a lovely, smooth, easy delivery.

Saturday

From 5.30 am to 7 am I had moderate contractions at about six to seven minute intervals. This is it, we thought, but the contractions slowed down and faded away. Spent the day shopping and went to see a film in the evening with only a few weak contractions.

11.00 pm   Contractions begin again in earnest, every nine to eleven minutes, lasting one minute or longer. Contractions start rather sharply, giving little time to put breathing into action, especially when I drift off to sleep between them, only to wake up in mid-contraction and struggle to stay on top. Some low backache which is helped by back-rubbing but Richard is finding it hard to stay awake and I feel mean waking him every ten minutes.

Sunday

Get up for bath and to wash hair, partly to relax, partly to relieve Richard and partly to take my mind off things now I'm sure I'm on the way. Contractions still at ten minute intervals and manageable with light breathing. After the bath – about 5 am – contractions become less regular and follow a pattern where the longer the gap between them the more severe the contraction. The gap is now anything between four and twenty-one minutes and they last 45 to 75 seconds.

6.00 am   Slight show at one of the very frequent visits to the loo.

8.15 am   Ring community midwife. I'm booked for a six hour Domino.* She is very reassuring, suggests sugary drinks – good to avoid ketosis.†

10.00 am   Midwife arrives, one I haven't met before at the clinic, but extremely sympathetic and reassuring. She says all is well and the cervix is very thin and stretchy but barely dilated, i.e. no more than on my previous clinic visit on Tuesday last. She is sympathetic about the broken sleep and suggests a mild sleeping pill to give me some rest and advises 'forgetting about labour for now'. She says she is very anti-medication herself and gives me one third of the usual dose. She says Welldorm will cross the placenta and could affect the baby, but since the birth is still a long way off it will be all gone by that time. She again stresses the need for sugar and we produce our glucose tablets. Also asks if we have got any

* With this system the community midwife comes to the woman's home, is with her during labour and goes into the hospital to deliver the baby. The mother and baby return home a few hours after. It stands for 'Domiciliary midwifery in and out'.

† see Glossary

raspberry leaf tea (we have) and suggests that I mix it with ordinary tea to make it more palatable and drink it every hour.

4.00 pm   Midwife calls back. I have had a sleep, contractions have died down, and I'm hungry. She says all is well and not to worry about glucose tablets if I feel I can eat. I do – cheese, yoghurt, bananas.

8.45 pm   Eat good supper. Breathing is difficult because contractions come on so sharply and strongly that I'm always being caught out and find it hard to breathe over the top. Bending over and having my lower back rubbed proves useful for backache.

11.15 pm   This seems to have been going on for ever and I have a cry as I feel so low. Contractions still about every ten minutes.

11.30 pm   Go to bed, but leap out again every ten minutes with Richard ditto to rub back. Frequent visits to loo.

Monday

2.00 am   Both get up for good as the getting up and down seems counter-productive. We listen to music and try to read. I'm feeling guilty again about disturbing Richard's rest and feel he's resenting me. He isn't, but it takes a while to sort it out.

4.00 am   Harmony reigns. Conscious relaxation of the pelvic floor during contractions helps. Still breathing through them. They are either five or six minutes apart and mild, or irregularly spaced and violent.

6.00 am   Contractions dying away and becoming milder. Sleep until

8.15 am   Contractions now feel lower and more concentrated in one place but are easier to breathe through as they follow the smooth curve I had been expecting instead of starting with a jagged edge.

9.15 am   Breakfast. Contractions all day are widely spaced but strong. Still breathing through them, bending over and having back rubbed. Try to catch up on some sleep. Get up and have bath at 5 pm.

7.00 pm   Can't face supper. Contractions now five to six minutes apart and lasting about a minute. Still bending over and back rubbing.

8.15 pm   Call midwife.

8.45 pm   Midwife says (different one) that I'm 3 cm dilated which is very disheartening in view of two sleepless nights and lots of work. Waters pronounced intact. After internal examination the contractions become more severe and come on so vigorously that shallow breathing is hard to get into. Shoulders getting tense. She offers hospital but says it may be a long time to go yet and we decide to stay at home.

9.45 pm   Very sick after a contraction. I try sitting up in bed to deal with contractions as it relaxes my shoulders and conserves some energy. Have had another Welldorm but think it's a mistake as contractions now sneak up on me without warning.

11.30 pm   Contractions at regular three-minute intervals.

Tuesday

1.00 am   Contractions now three to six minutes apart and of very variable intensity.

2.00 am   Both feeling desperate, we discuss the possibility of going into hospital in order just to settle in, but decide against it. Backache and the impossibility of either of us getting any sleep are the worst problems. I try sitting facing the back of a hard chair, but no help. It seems that what relieves the backache makes the contraction more painful and vice versa! Staying cheerful is very hard and contractions are still irregular and unpredictable.

5.45 am   Ring midwife again as we have both had enough and would be relieved to go to hospital. Starting to feel very shut-in at home and uncertain of what is happening. Community midwife is to meet us at the hospital. We feel instantly better having made a positive decision.

6.20 am   Arrive hospital. Community midwife has got out notes the night before and pinned inside our 'recipe' for what we would like to happen during the birth. Later this proves to be a key move! Immediate tactical error: the midwife has not yet arrived and the labour-ward sister separates us while I'm examined. We both keep asking to be together but it takes half an hour before we meet again in the labour room. The staff very nice and gave Richard a cup of tea and a running report, but it isn't the same as being together. I'm 4 cm dilated and the cervix is soft. I have said I would rather not be shaved and this is fine, and they decide I don't need an enema, having been to the loo repeatedly during the night. I'm torn between staying in a lovely hot bath and wanting to be with Richard – I get no response when I ask if he can be with me, so I'm reluctantly forced out of the bath. When I dry myself I discover I'm quite bloody. I'm alarmed but I'm told it's just a show.

The delivery room is pleasantly dim, contractions about every four minutes lasting 50 to 60 seconds. Backache still a real problem but a beanbag on the bed provides relief for a while. The midwife tutor whom we met at antenatal classes pops in – she is lovely and reassuring. Very positive and able to offer hints on what we might try. Nothing is forced on us and we feel very lucky to be here and to be allowed to continue in our own time. Tutor suggests dinner time as the expected hour of arrival. I'm given sugar water to drink as I'm ketotic and have said I want to avoid drips if possible. I burp regularly at the end of each contraction, but manage to keep drinking!

We have a tape recorder and enjoy music throughout the day.

9.40 am   Our own community midwife comes on duty. I knew she was off all weekend, and am very thrilled indeed to have her here now as we know she is very much in sympathy with our ideas on natural childbirth.

10.50 am   5 to 6 cm dilated. Examination again provokes a stormy period of contractions and violent backache. Try various positions and end up back to front astride a hard chair with a pillow on the back to lean on. 'Our' midwife improvises an ice pack and tentatively tries it on my back. I approve! Contractions still irregular but averaging four minutes, some very powerful. Try to sing but I can't manage it as

I can't get enough air to begin. Find ourselves counting backwards through heavy contractions.

11.30 am   Use gas and air for the first time. It's very helpful if I can time it right but I'm usually a little too slow, or occasionally too soon, and catch the end of the contraction as it wears off. I don't like to take more than three to four breaths as I then feel woozy. Generally a good thing, however.

1.15 pm   Very strong contractions – a few cries.

2.35 pm   8 cm dilated. 'Our' midwife is under pressure from the labour ward staff (senior sister we later learn is very pro-monitors and technology). We don't realize but later learn that there is some rivalry between hospital and community staff as the former regard the latter as being 'from the bogs'. 'Our' midwife is told whenever she takes a break (rare and brief) that 'of course it will end up with forceps'. She, bless her, is protecting us from all this! She suggests ARM unless we strongly object, and we agree, as we're getting pretty stretched now anyway.

3.02 pm   Very sick.

3.45 pm   First desire to push.

4.00 pm   Contractions very prolonged and powerful. Try sitting on loo, walking, kneeling, but always return to back of the chair. Welter of contractions.

6.05 pm   Pronounced to be at start of second stage but then all slows down and contractions stop.

6.55 pm   Internal examination – all OK – fully dilated – but no contractions. Only a few would do it we were told.

7.20 pm   Attached to dextrose drip to see if blood sugar boost will get contractions going.

8.10 pm   Attached to Syntocinon [uterine stimulant] as contractions have ceased. Exhausted.

8.20 pm   Suddenly all the things we didn't want are happening – dozens of strangers, white coats, all the technology wheeled in, machines bleeping (damn pump on drip wouldn't work and kept setting off alarms). I feel I have lost support from Richard and my midwife and am alone. They try a belt monitor but as I am now kneeling on the bed over a beanbag they can't get it in place.

Our lovely midwife keeps using her stethoscope and at each

listen pronounces the heartbeat strong and good. She invites a colleague to do another internal exam just to check all is OK, though she thinks it is. Extremely painful exam which makes me tense up for the first time. This is repeated by the houseman and they pronounce that the head is transverse and will have to be turned by forceps unless it straightens in the next couple of contractions. I feel terrible, out of control, in real pain and distress for the first time. The houseman then says he will give us 15 minutes as he knows we don't want intervention unless necessary (thank God for our recipe!) and leaves us. 'Our' midwife says, very quietly, – she has been silent through all the bustle and whispered consultations – 'It's not transverse, you know. It never has been. You are going to get this baby out yourself.'

I kneel between contractions and squat on the bed during them – feeling slightly unsafe. I've forgotten about the gas and air now and with much pushing and gasping I feel the head descending. It's awful and marvellous to push at the same time. My perineum burns and I would love to stop. I think I pass some faeces, but am not in a position to care. All I want to do is get this baby out safe and without forceps. I ask at one point how many more contractions it will take and our midwife says six. I count to four and then lose count. Now that all is progressing, the hospital staff melt away and I have Richard on one side and our midwife on the other.

At about 9.12 pm our midwife suggests I should turn over to watch the head. Richard puts up the mirror, having been shown how to do it by the tutor midwife 12 hours ago! I turn over and see the head already bulging from my vagina. I didn't know it was so far down. I touch the top of the baby's head in joy.

9.15 pm   Head crowns. Midwife says 'push.' I say, 'I can't.' She says, 'you can.' I don't really remember what I did. Apparently I cooperated because our baby is born and I have no cut. (Houseman had *told* her to do an episiotomy but she wasn't going to even if I tore!) No tear, no stitches. I feel her head born like a champagne cork coming out, though the midwife said it was well controlled. She cries as soon as her head is born. At the next contraction her body is born and delivered on to my belly at 9.25 pm. At 9.35 pm the cord is clamped and cut – she can't suck as she is very mucusy though pink, active and breathing well. Given syntometrine – so I'm told – though I didn't feel it. The placenta is delivered by controlled cord traction. Very bewildered but marvellously happy. Baby Rosemary sucked out, then held by dad and suckled by mum. Lovely!

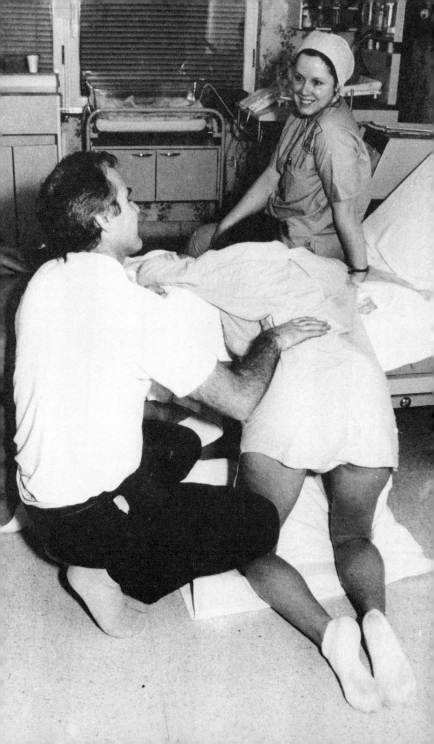

A Whirlwind Birth

What happens if a child finds being at a birth more than he or she can handle emotionally? What if the woman is overpowered by the contractions and feels that she is no longer in control? Birth is an overwhelming psychosexual experience and we cannot know exactly how we will behave or how we shall feel.

In this account a woman describes a tempestuous transition phase and a very rapid second stage which swept through her with such force that she did not even know whether or not her other child was in the room, and cried out with every contraction. The eight-year-old boy found this too much to take and very sensibly asked to go out of the room. He missed the birth but was back in before the cord was cut. He very much wants to be there for another birth.

I had my first baby eight years ago. I didn't go to NCT classes and knew virtually nothing of the birth process. I was induced when I was five days overdue, which I didn't like, although it was an easy three and a half hour birth, and I was very concerned that I shouldn't be induced this time. I was therefore really pleased when at six days overdue I had a show when I got up in the morning, and contractions. They were coming very fast, every three to five minutes, but only lasting about five or ten seconds. This didn't follow any standard pattern so I phoned the hospital and asked for their opinion. They didn't think anything was imminent, but said I could go in as soon as I felt like it. While I was pregnant I thought I would panic as soon as contractions started and rush off to hospital, but in fact it was obvious that nothing was going to happen for a while so we phoned my mother to tell her things had started, my sister Jenny, who was coming from London to look after Piers (my son) during the birth, and went shopping all morning. The contractions slowed down to every ten minutes or so but gradually got more uncomfortable, and at 2 pm we went to the hospital.

We had chosen the hospital specifically because they were willing to have my son at the birth, although they were very dubious about it and really didn't think it was a good idea. It was at their suggestion that I had my sister there too, to make sure Piers was OK and take him out if need be.

When we arrived at the hospital I was taken to a small room to be examined. My husband, Ross, and Piers came too, and the nurse explained to Piers what the fetal heart monitor was for and why I was being examined. I was only about 3 cm dilated so I went up to one of the wards to await developments. I changed into my own nightdress and dressing gown and settled down with a book and pencil and paper to time contractions, while Ross and Piers went home for lunch. They returned about 4 pm with Jenny and we sat around talking for an hour or so, timing contractions and discussing babies and hospitals. At 5.15 pm they went off to McDonald's for supper and I had hospital spaghetti on toast – or tried to – in between contractions which were now coming every three or four minutes, were very strong and painful, and lasting about 40 seconds. I gave up on the spaghetti and returned to bed. My entourage returned at 6.15 pm. I was examined and found to be 7 cm dilated and wheeled off to the delivery room.

At this point all my NCT training came unstuck, although the detailed knowledge of all that was happening to me made it much easier to bear. The contractions were incredibly strong. I hadn't realized the body was capable of such force. I had absolutely no control over the situation and didn't choose any of the birth positions so carefully rehearsed at classes. I just lay where I landed when I climbed from the wheelchair to the delivery bed, which was on my side with my legs curled up, hanging on to Ross when the contractions overpowered me. I had no idea if Piers and Jenny were in the room or not. Jenny told me afterwards that Piers asked to go and they went off for a walk around the hospital. I reached the transition stage at about 6.45 pm. It was unmistakable, I was shaking uncontrollably all over.

Because the second stage was nothing at all like the descriptions I had read I probably didn't cope as well as I might have done if I'd realized what was happening. Nature decided to speed things up and Camilla was born in about five minutes. I took no active part in the proceedings at all; there was no question of my breathing 'properly' and bearing down, my body just took over and pushed and I could only pant very fast and cope with each pain as it came. Because I knew the second stage could last an hour or more I was scared that this level of pain would go on and on and I wouldn't be able to cope. I didn't know that Camilla was arriving fast. Ross hadn't realized I didn't know what was happening and I was beyond asking! She was born at 6.55 pm, half an hour after I'd left the labour ward. The cord was wrapped round her neck and had to be freed immediately before her shoulders were born, then she was put straight on to my tummy. She was wrapped in a blanket, I put her to my breast and she sucked straight away and continued sucking happily for at least 20 minutes.

I didn't have any painkillers; I tried gas and air but it didn't make any difference, it just made me feel light headed so I didn't use it again. I didn't tear so didn't have to have stitches.

Piers was back with me by now; he had missed the actual birth by only two minutes and that because it had all happened so fast. He came back when Camilla was lying on my tummy. He saw the cord being cut and the afterbirth being born and wasn't at all upset by the mess. He told me that he left when he did, not because he was scared or upset at the time, but because he didn't know whether he might be upset later at the sight of the blood and general mess. He was only out of the room for five minutes and had already experienced the worst there was to happen, which was my crying at the peak of each contraction.

Looking back now there is no doubt that he could have stayed with me the whole time. It was a great shame that he missed the moment of birth, the 'best bit'.

Now, three months later, Piers is excellent with Camilla. He picks her up and handles her with great confidence, talks to her, plays with her to make her laugh, and as far as I can tell shows no jealousy or resentment, despite being the only child for eight years.

I am very glad I had the courage of my convictions and encouraged Piers in his wish to be with me, despite the lack of help or encouragement from doctors, midwives, hospitals and even the NCT. There is no doubt that he's glad he was there and is disappointed that he missed the moment of birth. He will definitely be there next time round!

Piers writes about his sister's birth

Mummy had a show in the morning of the 27 September but her contrations weren't very strong so we went into Swindon (our nerest town) and shoped until about two o'clock. Then went to our hospital. We waited in the waiting room until we were called and Mummy and my stepfather and I all went into a small room with one bed and a big light. Mummy lay on the bed and a womon asked Mummy a few questions and cheked a few things with a machine on wheels. Then she lefed and a few more womin came and did the same thing by this time I felt exited. Then the last womon came and showed us the ward that Mummy would be in and then Ross (my stepfather) and I went home and found Jenny (my Aunt) who we had phoned that morning and had lunck with her and then we went back to the hospitol and found Mummy and stayed there and the midwife checed Mummy every now and then. (I didn't know if I liked it or not at the moment.) A bit later Mummy had supper. Then Jenny, Ross and I went to Mcdonelds for our supper. When we got back Mummy's contractions were quite strong now. A bit later we all went to the delivery room. Mummy's contractions were coming every fifty secands now and I wanted to leave because I was scared so I asked Jenny if she could take me out so she did for about five minutes and we went for a little walk around the coradoors. Then we came back in at about ten seconds after Camilla was born and I saw the cord being cut and I saw the after birth. I mist the part when she was actwaly born though. The two days before Mummy came home we visited her and Camilla. Then on Monday we picked her up and came home. Im sure I would like to see the next birth.

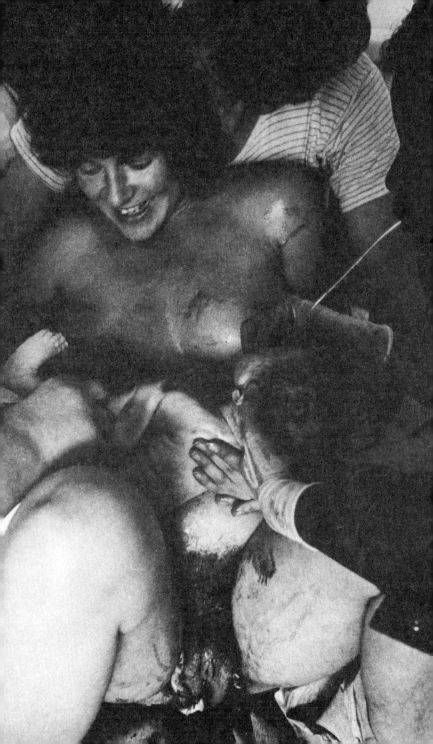

A Shared Experience

Here is a couple who were very together throughout the birth of their baby. Tony was in touch with Claire's feelings in such a sensitive way that his presence turned a birth experience which could have been traumatic into one about which both of them feel very positive. I start with Tony's birth account because it provides the bare bones of what happened. As you read Claire's account you can see exactly how Tony helped, as well as various things done by other people which interrupted the flow of feeling and events and made labour more difficult for Claire.

Tony's story of the birth

Claire and I both seemed to wake up at 10 am and then before having a chance to say much Claire exclaimed in a very calm voice, 'Oh, I think my waters have gone.' Sure enough, there was a small wet patch. I got up and tried to think about what was the best thing to go for. I decided to have a cup of tea and stick on a record. I made Claire's breakfast and did myself some toast.

Next thing contractions were coming and so she sat on a pail with a towel draped over it to aid relaxation of her pelvic floor. By this time she'd already had a bit of diarrhoea and a show of mucus. She still managed to tell me how to spell diarrhoea and was breathing over her contractions very naturally and with what seemed great ease.

We stayed at the house for another hour. Claire had most of her stuff ready, and after shoving it all in the car we drove to the hospital, arriving at 12 midday.

We were met by a midwife and went into the bathroom which also doubled as an examination room. Claire was examined by the midwife and told she was about 2.5 cm dilated. Her contractions were coming every two minutes.

After the examination, Claire sat on a pail with a monitor and an equally insensitive piece of equipment called a medical student appeared on the scene.

A mother greets her baby; the midwife is sucking out the baby's airways – something which is often done unnecessarily.

After the monitor was fixed up we tried just to concentrate on each other and chat. The machine proved very unreliable, losing contact with the baby's heart-rate at every contraction, and was a distraction we could have done without – especially as the baby's heart-rate was consistent for the whole 40 minutes (142 beats per minute) and there were no signs of distress. What happened to the plastic horn they seemed quite happy to use down in the clinic?

After 40 minutes we were taken upstairs. Although this felt better, it wasn't possible to move around, as we were in this enclosed space in the ward – bed, curtains and table. I decided to get us moving around, and so we walked to a small roof garden in the hospital. Claire was doing fine. Whilst out in the garden she found it useful to lean on the rails surrounding it during contractions.

2 pm – Back into the ward. Claire found it useful to stay on the bed in an all-fours position or kneel and support herself with her arms round my neck. After about 30 minutes we went for another walk, this time just along the corridor as the contractions seemed strong and more frequent. We went back to the bed and she got into the same position, me standing and Claire holding on to me from the bed. It was now about 3 pm and she was having one strong contraction followed by a smaller one with very little time in between. This, I'm sure, was the transition period into second stage.

The midwife on the ward had been poking her head round the curtains and asking whether everything was all right, mainly because of the loud groaning which was coming from Claire, who was worried that she was disturbing the other women's afternoon tea. Finally she gave Claire an internal, and looked round at me and said, 'Oh, she's about 9 cm dilated, I'd better phone for a porter!' The porter arrived with a wheelchair and it seemed like the building was on fire. Claire got on to the chair, he sped off down the corridor, followed by one of the midwives, and then there was me tagging along, bags dangling from my arms.

The student nurse, medical student and the other midwife helped Claire on to the bed. At this point she was trying to strip off her dress and was asked if she minded waiting until the porter had gone as they didn't like it!

3.25 pm – Claire was kneeling on the bed and holding on to the bottom end rail with her head next to mine. I was standing at the end of the bed encouraging and caressing her. After about 15 minutes she said she wasn't comfortable in this position, and so I suggested she move into the squatting position. The midwife and I supported her and let her rest between contractions. This was the worst part for her, because every time she sat back she felt her coccyx being pressed uncomfortably on the bed and had to try to relieve this by pushing herself off the bed with one arm.

The midwives then explained to Claire that she should now start pushing. I could see that she was getting a lot of strain in her face and neck, and so told her to try and open up. This helped and she then started to get the pushing located more in the bottom half of her body than the top. The baby's head appeared after about 40 minutes, which was marvellous. Claire touched it. She'd had doubts as to whether there was enough room. After about six more pushes, the baby's head was out and moving. It was an emotional time and she did one more push and the baby's body came.

The midwife started to suction the baby, but stopped after I asked whether the baby was all right and whether this was necessary. The baby was then put on Claire's chest and at this point I cut the cord after it had stopped pulsating.

Claire's labour story

Still in bed at 10 am after a night out visiting friends (our last planned outing before EDD) I was awakened by my waters breaking – lovely hot trickling. No thought of panic, just calmly told Tony. Normally he is extremely unresponding in the morning, very difficult to rouse, and usually aggressive when he does become conscious. Instead, he threw off the bedclothes, donned a dressing gown and started doing incredibly useful things – brought the pail for me to stand over in case of a deluge, made breakfast, and started looking through our labour plan. It was a wonderful start to the day – I felt we were both very well prepared and in control of the situation. I went to the loo and stayed there for some time with diarrhoea, a bit of mucus and a couple of light contractions. It all felt really good physically.

I had a shower, washed my hair, and had breakfast with muesli, peaches and coffee. Then I phoned the hospital and felt pleased that I was able to do this myself. I was told to report in immediately and to bring everything with me. Because my waters had broken I wouldn't be allowed home before the baby was born. I felt an unspoken implication that maybe it would be some time before the baby was born, but the midwife's voice was very confidence-inspiring and so I didn't get worried about it. In any case, I was by now having contractions every two to three minutes, and so was sure that I was actually in labour. The contractions were like the sensation of a heavy period. I've never really had period 'pains' but I have experienced this muscle contraction in a milder form before – very low down, in a horizontal band where a bikini should be.

Having to go to hospital quickly was disappointing, as we'd planned to stay at home as long as possible. But I was determined not to rush things, especially as I knew from the amount of leakage that only the front waters had escaped and that there was no crisis. So, I put on Bob Marley – loud – and tried to calmly get organized. I was feeling excited by now, like just before guests arrive for a party, and was very glad I'd made so many lists. I didn't ever refer to the labour plan, but I did need to check what still had to go into my case. We phoned our parents to let them know.

I started to make another call but for the first time a contraction felt a good bit stronger – not painful, but I couldn't have coped with the phone call. Luckily Tony wasn't far away and he took over. All this time I'd been either on the lavatory, the pail or walking about. Contractions felt most comfortable sitting on the pail. If I was caught walking about, I found the most helpful thing to do was to lean against something and do a bit of pelvic rocking.

By 11.30 am we were all ready to go. I felt very strange going out to the car. We live on a main road which is always busy, and I was conscious of the rest of the world and glad I'd put on sunglasses. It wasn't that sunny – I simply felt the need to retreat behind something. I kept wondering whether people would know I was in labour. I had a few more contractions in the car – nothing dramatic – and still managed to navigate us. I was actually pleased to be making the journey at that point. Although staying at home for longer would have been nice, I felt that a car journey might not have been pleasant at a later stage in labour. When we parked outside the hospital I had to lean against the car roof for another contraction. It felt strange doing this in the street, but I didn't really care. There was still no pain, just a feeling that I had to do nothing but relax as much as possible to let the muscle contract.

At 12 midday we arrived in the labour ward. A very nice midwife, Denise, and a student nurse, Meg, met us. We were taken into the admission room, with a lavatory, bath and couch. Denise was a soft-spoken, gentle woman who explained everything very thoroughly – I took to her quickly. Meg was similar and seemed very young. I found it interesting listening to the teaching which went on. The internal was OK but I felt a bit of pain while Denise poked about. 2.5 cm didn't seem much to me, and I was disappointed to learn that I'd only got that far. I allowed Meg to do an internal examination, something I never thought would happen. She was so nice I was only too happy to help out, and she thanked me very politely later when she went off duty.

By now I was in a hospital gown which was very uncomfortable – it was really tight across my throat and I spent most of the time holding it away from there as it added to a feeling of nausea which was beginning to come with each contraction. We were moved to a delivery room – not our own room with a Borning bed as I'd been led to expect, but one with an old-fashioned delivery table. I was back on the pail before anyone had a chance to get me anywhere else. The monitor arrived and was attached. It felt fairly uncomfortable, and Denise explained what it was doing, but before long I'd had enough. I couldn't stop watching it. Every time I had a contraction there was a loss of contact with the fetal heart! Before I felt each contraction the monitor showed that one was on the way. I hated this warning that one was coming. It made me tense up mentally and made it harder work to stay relaxed physically. It was much easier just to 'feel' everything. The machine was a dead loss. I was on it for about 40 minutes instead of the usual 20 because they couldn't get it to do what they wanted. It didn't register one incredibly strong contraction – the first one where I had to do a bit of slow breathing – and then it did a huge peak on the graph for a mild one. I was considering asking to come off it. By this time I was leaning on the delivery table for contractions. I don't know whether they ever got what they wanted from the machine, but at last I was unplugged.

The room was filling up. A woman medical student arrived at the same time as the change of shift. Mary, the new midwife, was very large, jolly and quite a different personality from Denise. I wasn't sure that I liked her so much, but tried not to pass judgement. Jo, the medical student, said she'd be there 'until the bitter end even if it took till 4 am.' I decided I did not like her! Apart from reminding me that I might be there for hours, she fiddled a lot with the monitoring devices, and, worst of all, talked to Tony while I was having contractions.

I was worried about thoughts of older women and their long painful labours and presumed that I was in for a 12-hour one at least. It seemed like a long time to go!

Then we were taken upstairs to the antenatal ward. I was shown to a bed, sheets invitingly folded back hotel-style, and desperately wanted to lie down and go to sleep. I was not feeling too happy and knelt on the bed feeling very weary. Tony drew the curtains round in an attempt to have some privacy and we tried to look at a book of pictures. I couldn't concentrate on this at all. I felt nauseous during most contractions and couldn't stop worrying about being sick and how long I was going to be in labour. I'd definitely stopped enjoying it by now!

Tony was marvellous. I didn't really want him to do much and didn't feel like talking and was concerned that he might not feel he was being much help. Since we'd arrived in hospital he'd kissed and cuddled me a lot – even when other people were around – and that was wonderful. He sometimes stroked me gently during contractions, but what I wanted was to be touched firmly – movement was an irritation. I saw him refer to the labour plan occasionally, and could hear him dealing with the staff well and asking questions. I was happy to let him take charge now and felt very confident in what he was doing. It helped so much and allowed me to concentrate on my body. What I was trying to do was to relax as much as possible and to stay upright and let my uterus do its work. I was really aware of what was happening inside. I can't describe it as pain, but it was frightening to have no control over part of my body. However, it was satisfying to be able to consciously relax the rest of me. Breathing was nice and slow, too.

I was restless and Tony suggested getting dressed again and going for a walk. Brilliant idea! We went on to the roof garden. I sent him to get a chair from the antenatal classroom, one that I knew from experience would be comfortable when I faced the back of it. He made himself a cup of tea and we sat in a shady corner. I told him he was helping a lot, even though I didn't want him to do much. Just his presence was a strength. I was worried that he might be feeling left out.

It didn't seem long before I wanted to go back inside. It was still and hot out there and I was conscious of overlooking windows, but basically it was this restless feeling again – like a fractious child. I couldn't settle to doing anything for long. Poor Tony – but at least he managed to get down his cup of tea. It was good that he knew the hospital so well. He'd been to virtually all my clinic appointments and nearly all the antenatal classes so he knew all about making cups of tea in the classroom and about the existence of this roof-garden area.

Back to the antenatal ward and that inviting bed! I so wanted to lie down on it and go to sleep. But soon Tony suggested another walk and even talked about having a bath! To me the prospect seemed too exhausting for words but I was happy to do what he suggested. This second walk only got us a few yards along the corridor. I had a big contraction while leaning against an open window sill watching an incredibly peaceful scene below of some geriatric patients sitting under the trees in the sun and a cat sunning himself on a doorstep. Back to the antenatal ward.

Instead of just the bikini tension with contractions they now involved the whole uterus. It was great being able to feel so well what was happening. I was very conscious of the muscle pushing down and had a good image of the baby and what was happening to it. However, I was beginning to think that I couldn't cope for much longer and was upset to find myself thinking about epidurals at what was supposedly such an early stage in my labour. I didn't mention this to Tony, but thought that we'd have to discuss it before long and was not looking forward to that.

I was now getting two contractions close together – a very strong one followed by a weaker one. I was kneeling on the bed pulling on the bed-head railings with my hands and had started doing vocalized breathing. This was a wonderful aid. It gave me something positive to do, and something to listen to. It was merely an extension of the slow breathing I'd been doing up till now, and it seemed a natural development to start vocalizing it. I probably wouldn't have felt comfortable about doing it unless I'd heard Johanna, my childbirth teacher, demonstrating it in class. I just copied the sounds she'd made and tried not to think about the other poor women in the ward on bed rest trying to read their magazines or have an afternoon nap. Tony hadn't said much for a bit, and I was very busy getting on with what I was doing. But I noticed that he was reading the labour plan again and that he was devouring the page about transition. It struck me as ridiculous and although I said nothing to him I thought he was being incredibly hopeful, if not downright panicky. I was convinced that I was still only in the early stages and was really sure that before long we'd be debating about an epidural. I don't know what his conclusions were but he fed me a couple of spoonfuls of honey which was great.

A midwife arrived to examine me. I expected to be told I was 3 cm dilated and making too much fuss. I wasn't keen to leave my bed-head for the examination, and indeed by now just turning round and opening my legs was a great effort and took a lot of energy. A quick examination and she said I was 9 cm dilated and had better go downstairs! I had to get her to repeat it, and was so pleased, I smiled for the first time in ages. Things really got moving now. A porter arrived and I heaved myself on to the wheelchair. The curtains were whisked back and I managed a bit of a joke to the lady in the next bed about leaving her in peace to read – she was totally unmoved. Not surprising, I suppose. If she had weeks of lying in bed to look forward to, I must have been the last thing she wanted to see/hear. Still, maybe she'll remember my breathing when her time comes.

The porter sped off along the corridor. I was concerned about Tony not being by my side. I presume he was struggling along behind with all the bags. It would have been nicer to have made the journey to the delivery room at a more leisurely pace, but I suppose porters don't like ladies giving birth on their wheel-chairs! I was met in the lift by Denise – who should have been going off duty by then. She gave me a lovely warm welcome, and we joked about the necessity of getting a pail for the labour ward so that everyone could enjoy quick labours! As we approached the corridor to the delivery room I felt another contraction beginning. I started moaning and hoped that the porter would stop so that I could cope with the contraction in peace – but of course the poor man doubled speed! As we entered our delivery room I was taking my dress off over my head while still in the wheelchair. There was a general feeling all round that I shouldn't be doing this – apparently something was said but I don't remember that – I was only aware of disapproving looks. Honestly, one minute they're in a hurry, hurtling me along at top speed in a wheelchair – next minute they want to wait for reasons of supposed 'decency'. I found they were strangely obsessed by modesty. I suspect that women who deliver totally naked are not all that common. At some stage after the birth they tried to cover up my abdomen and legs with cloth and I refused. Brazen hussy!

Getting up on the bed seemed a gargantuan effort, but I made it. Don't remember how. Thank goodness Tony was close by again and telling me what to do. I took up position on all fours facing the bottom of the bed, my hands on the wooden bed frame, my head on Tony's shoulder. For contractions I pushed myself up on my hands and Tony spoke into my ear. He said all the right things and I was very tuned in to what he was telling me. Having such close physical contact was very reassur-ing. It was really being embraced and having a shoulder to lean on at the same time.

The room was full of people. Both midwives were in attendance. Denise had decided to stay on and I was very glad that she did, so that I was not in the position of having to get to know someone new at a time when everything was such an effort. Denise seemed to be in charge and did most of the talking to me; Mary assisted, and proved to be a tower of strength and quickly had my trust; Jo, the medical student, interfered, fiddled around with the monitor trying to get a fetal heart reading, again without success, and was totally out of touch with everyone in the room.

From this point on I was very much more malleable and would have swung from a chandelier had anyone asked me to. Mentally, I was still in control, but lacked the will-power to stay in charge. No one said I was 10 cm dilated and in second stage. They were presuming that I should be pushing and started asking why I wasn't doing so. Tony was still very together and was giving me sensible advice about opening up, relaxing and breathing slowly. When I started pushing I did so gently as my childbirth teacher had taught us; the sounds she'd used to demonstrate what it might be like were very useful. It felt good to me but the midwives weren't happy with my progress and didn't think I was making enough effort. They thought I was pushing in my throat.

Denise had a pelvic girdle model and was trying to show me what was going on inside. It all began to seem preposterous and I kept telling them all that there was no room. Tony reminded me of a quotation I'd read in a book, *Spiritual Midwifery* written by the midwives on The Farm in Tennessee – 'Your brain doesn't know how to give birth, but your monkey does.' He said something like 'remember your monkey.' I made a few monkey noises and we laughed – God knows what the others thought. No one passed comment! I was beginning to feel more together, even though the pushing was not to their liking. It was very difficult to get any sensation of what was happening in the vagina. I just felt that I wanted to defecate and started telling everyone this in between contractions. I'd been sipping water on and off since being in the antenatal ward and was now getting very thirsty. Tony produced the sponge. He stuck this in my mouth at my next request for water, but I spat it out and demanded a proper drink! Denise soaked a huge handful of rough paper towels in water and squeezed them out over my face and head. It felt fantastic.

I felt I was getting nowhere, mainly because the midwives were not happy with my pushing, but also because, in spite of being comfortable, being on all fours didn't give me any feeling of strength. Tony suggested squatting and so with another monumental effort I changed position. As I sat back on the Borning bed I was upset to see a tiny amount of excreta on the bed and also on my leg. The midwives were not at all interested but cleaned it up. For the next contraction I pushed up into a squat, one arm round Tony's shoulder, one round Mary's. The student nurse took over from Mary who scrubbed up and did the delivery, but I was unaware of the changeover. Jo really went to work now with the fetal heart monitor and was poking it all over the place trying to make contact. Denise told her to stop and only to monitor during contraction. They all started making a lot of noise during contractions. I'm not convinced that this was helpful, and was more encouraged by Denise's pep talks in between. She correctly guessed that I was frightened of something (the apparent impossibility of it all) and treated me like an intelligent human being. Tony, too, was encouraging – and it was nice when he took his shirt off and we had skin contact, although I suspect he did it because of the heat. The others laughed when I suggested we should all be topless. His presence was so important. He moved away to get some water. I felt a contraction starting and shouted for him to come back, feeling desperate because he'd left my side for even a second.

It was nice that contractions were becoming more spaced out now. There was time in between them to make jokes, have a cuddle and get in a good mood – and I felt glad each time a contraction came as it meant the baby was closer to being born.

At one point there was a really long pause. They were all standing around virtually twiddling their thumbs and I got some energy back and mentally got myself together. It was after this that I began to get a bit of praise. I was working very hard and couldn't imagine how Tony and the nurses were managing to stay upright under my weight. I was pressing down hard on their shoulders, but all the fears I'd had about a supported squat being uncomfortable were totally unfounded. Somehow they both got it just right, height, angle, everything. Relaxing in between squats was much more difficult. Leaning back on the Borning bed was the obvious thing to do, that's what it had been designed for after all, but it was uncomfortable. The pressure on my coccyx was intense, much more painful than a contraction, and so I ended up pushing myself up on my hands.

I soon started to feel a stinging sensation. I'd got into a state of waiting for instructions and presumed that the midwives would know what was happening and would tell me if I should stop pushing. Instead, I was still being encouraged. I felt the baby's head and looked at it in a mirror. It was the most extraordinary feeling because it was as if I was touching part of myself. Soon after that I gave a terrifically strong push – I had been holding myself back a bit until then, and I remember thinking, 'All right, if they want me to push harder, I'll show them.' It felt fantastic. I could feel the head and then the rest of the body slithering out.

The baby was handed to me, all blue and gurgling. What a feeling! Tony was overcome – looked like he didn't know whether to laugh or cry. Even so he was still very cool – told the midwife to stop suctioning the baby as she was doing OK and managed to jump in to cut the cord. There had been no time to discuss any of this, and at the time of admission there had been the feeling of hours to spare, but he coped incredibly well and managed to do most of the things he'd planned. I couldn't have cared less by now, but was impressed that I was shown the syntometrine and was asked if it was OK for it to be administered. I was told when the placenta was being delivered and was pleased to get a good look at it. So big – and it actually looked like the funny plastic model they had in the antenatal class. Denise explained it all to us and showed us the different parts. I really appreciated her explanations. Tanya was weighed, measured and dressed in a hospital gown. 8 lb 9 oz.

I was told that I had a second degree tear and that a doctor would come to stitch it up. As it turned out a lovely Irish midwife was given the job. At Tony's prompting I dared to ask if she'd had any experience, and was delighted to be told she'd had more than the doctors. She was marvellous and talked through the whole procedure, again explaining exactly what she was doing. Tony held Tanya against his naked chest and bravely watched a lot of what was going on. I had a look at the finished result which was pretty gruesome, if neat, and was glad I hadn't seen the tear itself. As the stitching was going on Tony was able to spend time alone with Tanya which I enjoyed watching. We were also able to sit closely, the three of us, and she looked very intently at us both and around the room. When I put her to my breast the midwife did make a joke about the difficulty of working on a moving target, but she never suggested that anything we were doing was interfering with her work, and neither did we feel inhibited by her presence.

We were asked if we'd like to spend some time alone together and we said yes, but it didn't happen. It would have been nice. Jo was the first person to barge in. Typical! She just hung about by the bed doing nothing and obviously hadn't been told what was going on. Tony told her there was some rubbish in the sink which needed clearing up. We had some tea, Tony got our food from the car and took some photographs. Next arrival was a nurse to give me a wash and so Tony decided to make a few phone calls. The nurse held Tanya while I washed my upper body and as I was trying to manoeuvre one of my feet into the basin of water Tony returned. I asked him to help me wash my feet and thought he'd give them a quick dunk. Instead he embarked on an incredibly ritualistic washing of feet – it was a wonderful feeling, very spiritual and he got very involved in it. I'll never forget those few minutes.

Tony and I were pleased with ourselves and the way we'd handled labour. As regards the hospital I think my second stage was slightly mismanaged. It was upon us so suddenly that we did well to keep as much control as we did, and at least Tony was able to get me into the right positions. I'm sure the tear could have been avoided, as it was caused by the baby's shoulders, not her head. I could have helped a lot here but was waiting to be told not to push. If I'd been shouted at a little less enthusiastically I might not have pushed quite so hard.

The fetal monitor was a disaster and seemed to me not to be doing what it was supposed to do. I wasn't worried that anything was wrong with the baby, but having to sit there for 40 minutes while they fiddled about made it difficult to maintain my composure. It was all happening at a time when contractions were frequent and getting strong enough to have to think about breathing, and everyone was tuned in to the machine and not to me. Ridiculous! The medical student was incredibly insensitive and didn't appear to know when I was having contractions. All the other staff, especially those wonderful midwives, are amazingly compassionate. I felt I'd known them for years. They had a gift of communication and understanding.

The postnatal experience was mixed. Labour seemed like a piece of cake compared to the days that followed. I wished I'd had a postnatal plan to refer to, like the labour plan. They gave conflicting advice and for the first few days I was at sea. However, because of the good-natured chaos, I felt that by the time I left hospital I was making all my own decisions mainly out of necessity. If you didn't learn to look after yourself I suppose someone would have come to your aid, but not before a few disasters. The one big complaint was the night staff. Someone new nearly every night. I felt at my most vulnerable at night.

The person I learned most from in hospital was another mother in the bed opposite mine. It was her second child and just watching how she behaved with her baby was incredibly beneficial to me. I picked up a lot, too, about general baby organization although it was all done by observation – we never had long chats about things like that. I felt she was a real friend and in many ways learned more about being a mother from watching her than from all the books I've read.

PART THREE

What is Birth Like for the Baby?

'The child's flesh is tender, soft, flaccid. Children that are newborn should be swathed in roses ground with salt. The roof of the mouth should be rubbed with one's finger wet in honey, to cleanse and comfort the inner part of the mouth, and also to excite and to kindle the child's appetite. And he should be oft bathed and anointed with oil of myrtle or of roses and all the limbs should be anointed and rubbed with this oil.'

(Bartholomaeus' advice to mediaeval parents)

Birth is not only an experience for the parents but for the baby who is coming to life too. In concentrating exclusively on the mother's and father's psychology on the one hand, or on hospital procedures and the routine practices which often make of birth something that seems to happen on an assembly line on the other, it is easy to forget the baby's special needs. These basic needs are not only for physical care, but for an environment in which its spontaneous urges to move, to look around, to fix its eyes on the shining eyes of its mother, to root and suckle, and above all to communicate, to give and respond to human signals, are able to take place smoothly. A newborn baby is not just a passive little package, a bundle of flesh, muscles, nerves and other tissues, but a living, sentient, social being from the first moments of life. If it is treated like a hunk of meat or an inanimate doll it is being as inadequately cared for in human terms as the baby who is allowed to get too cold or who is not fed. Human beings have the right to be treated like human beings from the very beginning.

Frédérick Leboyer* has focused attention on the baby's experience and on the way in which we welcome or fail to welcome our babies into the world. The baby is pressed and squeezed out of the uterus and down the birth canal in a relentless way, pummelled and gripped and twisted in its progress in a manner which may be just as painful and distress-

* *Birth Without Violence* (Fontana, 1977).

185

ing for the child as the contractions are for the mother who is giving birth. When there is pressure on the umbilical cord, oxygen-bearing blood is temporarily cut off or reduced in supply and the baby probably has a reduced awareness of what is happening. But in normal, vigorous labour the baby is a feeling participant in the act of birth, one who probably makes active head rocking and creeping movements to assist its progress down the birth canal, and is not just a passive passenger.

Leboyer is concerned about what he sees as the baby's ordeal and talks about the child being 'crushed in the birth canal' as it is 'thrust into this hell', and even goes so far as to call the mother who is subjecting her baby to this trauma 'the enemy' and 'a monster'.* One might think that if labour is harmful to babies, Caesarean section is the answer and out of kindness we ought to refuse to have our babies vaginally. Yet a baby who is just lifted out of the mother's body through an incision in the abdominal wall tends to be less alert to respond to life and usually requires some extra stimulus to breathe.

In normal labour the uterus massages the baby with each contraction, pressing amniotic fluid out of the respiratory passages so that they are clear to take in air with the first breath at delivery, and vigorously stimulating every part of the baby's body so that it slips out of the birth canal ready to respond to the challenge of living, and alert to adapt to its new environment.

Leboyer is highly critical of routine practices and thoughtless and insensitive behaviour in the delivery room which result in rough handling of the baby, loud noises and unco-ordinated, hurried movements. In many hospitals the haste to complete the third stage of labour, clear up, suture the perineum after the episiotomy and get the mother to the ward still takes precedence over more human considerations, and the bonding of not only mother and baby but of father and baby is allowed to take place only within a restricted space of time when they are permitted to hold their child.† This is terminated by whisking the baby away to the nursery to be examined by the

* Op. Cit. p. 185
†† *The New Good Birth Guide*, Sheila Kitzinger (Penguin, 1983).

paediatrician, and the mother may not see her child again for several hours or even longer. The unspoken message is clear: 'If you are going to be a good mother and are not going to mistreat your baby we must give you time for holding the baby, but this has to fit into hospital routines and only requires a few minutes or so.' Moreover, concern about possible baby battering means that now staff watch new mothers to see if they are bonding 'correctly' during this time, as if an examination in motherhood is being conducted in the minutes following delivery. I believe that while there is a real advantage in staff being sensitive to the nuances of the interaction between the mother and her new baby, this can only be achieved when there is understanding and compassion and should never become a mere bald notation of observations like 'Mother refused to hold baby' or 'Mother said, "What an ugly little thing!"' There is a great deal more to the first meeting of mother and baby than that!

Leboyer believes that the baby should be greeted in silence, born into silence and peace where no noise intrudes on the infant's first sensory contact with the world outside the uterus. He also suggests that lights should be dimmed so that no harsh light assaults the baby as it first attempts to open its eyes. Newborn babies are not blind, but blinded. Lighting in hospital delivery rooms is often excessively bright not only for the baby but also for the woman who is sometimes expected to labour with lamps shining full in her face. If attendants are anxious that they cannot see what is happening, a spot-light is sufficient to enable them to observe the perineum. There is rarely any need to have bright lighting which makes either the mother or the baby uncomfortable. In my experience babies differ in the way they respond to light at delivery. Many babies immediately screw up their eyes as if in pain and open them only when lights are dimmed. Since the baby needs to open its eyes to get in touch with its world, harsh lighting hampers it in its first reaching out to begin to know the environment.

The silence is another matter. The woman who wants a Leboyer-style delivery may feel inhibited about crying out in joy as her baby is delivered and both father and mother may be told 'sh, sh, sh' as they shout with wonder and delight as their baby bursts into life. I believe that to suppress spontaneous emotional expression during this peak psychological experience can do nothing but harm and that its denial must affect interaction between mother, father and baby in a negative way.

Because childbirth is for the woman a psychosexual experience, the emotional peak attained when her baby slips into life, the sense of physical release and the extraordinary feeling of the warm, wet, firm body between her legs is often accompanied by involuntary sounds of astonishment, pleasure and sometimes ecstasy. To interrupt or forbid these is to interfere in a climactic experience which is no less vivid and intense because it is the birth of a baby rather than the peak of love-making.

The act is completed in fulfilment and in a satisfaction which is the deeper because it is not only intellectual knowledge that the baby is here, nor only emotional in the sense that there is joy at welcoming the new life, but also intensely *physical.* The physical reality of childbirth, experienced in her body in the full drama of creation, is an integral part of the emotions that lead the mother to reach down to draw her baby into her arms and to know that she belongs to the child and the child to her.

Moreover, sound is not new to the baby. While inside the uterus the baby has been able to hear many sounds inside its mother's body and others coming from the outside world. These are conducted readily through the amniotic fluid in which the baby is lying, but because it also fills the middle ear they are probably muffled. Anyone who has heard the sounds of the mother's blood vessels chugging away will be aware that the baby is accustomed to a steady beat from the maternal aorta* and clearly it must also hear the rumblings and bursts of rhythmic activity in her digestive tract. The baby responds to loud noises coming from outside too. When a study was done in Warsaw over the Polish national holiday doctors found that the babies' heart rates changed every time cannon fired. They thought at first that this might have happened because the mothers were startled by the noise, so they fixed up the mothers with earphones so that they could listen to music and then used

---

* *Lullababy Womb Sound* Cassette (Kings Thorn, Hereford).

a tuning fork over their abdomens to discover whether the babies reacted to sounds.

Research showed that the fetus does respond to noise of specific kinds of intensity, pitch and tone, as any mother realizes who has noticed how her baby moves when she is listening to music, especially when cymbals clash or when sound reverberates. Dr Michel Odent, working in Pithiviers, France, introduced singing groups for couples during pregnancy because the audiologist in his team found that certain kinds of musical sound are most likely to stimulate a response in the fetus.* She calls these sounds 'pelvic' because they appear to resonate in the cavity of the pelvis. It is almost as if the baby dances in reaction to them. Dr Michèle Clements in London has discovered that the fetus actually appears to show preference for some kinds of music and that the same music when played to the newborn is most likely to soothe a crying baby.†

It seems that the uterus, far from being silent and completely cut off from the world, a pitch-dark cave isolated in the recesses of the mother's body, is actually a busy, bustling place where light filters through shadows and occasionally irradiates the outer dome, and which hums with noise both from the mother's own internal organs and from her voice and the voices and other sounds connected with activity going on around her. All this suggests that receiving the newborn baby into complete silence could be more of a shock than greeting it with human speech.

The baby is already familiar with the cadences of its mother's voice and possibly also with those of its father and other children in the family. Viewed in this light, nothing could be better than to welcome the child with its parents' own excited voices, and then for the mother to draw the baby up into her arms and nestle it close to her heart where it can hear the regular beat of a sound which it already knows well.

† *Birth Reborn*, Dr Michel Odent (Pantheon Books, New York, 1984).

* 'Observations on certain aspects of neonatal behaviour in response to auditory stimuli', paper delivered at 5th Int. Congress of Psychosomatic Obst. & Gynec., Nov. 1977, Rome.

Dr Michel Odent calls other intrusive, distracting sounds which are a normal part of life in a hospital 'parasitic' and believes that these are the ones which it is important to eradicate: heavy footsteps, instruments dropped in a kidney dish, voices of command, doors banging, telephones ringing, the impersonal sound of the intercom, squeaking, clattering trolleys and the chatter of people who are not focused on the reality of this unique moment as a baby comes to life and gazes at its parents for the first time.

The baby can hear most readily sound which corresponds to the tone of the human voice and especially the pitch of a woman's voice. When she speaks directly to her baby the mother often quite unconsciously raises the pitch of her voice so that it is several notes higher than her usual speaking voice. Not only the mother does this, but other women do it too; they are speaking in normal voices and then one turns to the baby and says, 'Hello sweetie, you're a nice baby, a poppet!' and suddenly her voice is dramatically different, pitched precisely to elicit the best response from the newborn baby. Men do this too, but perhaps more rarely. In a tape recording of one of my own children's births my husband can be heard first speaking to me, 'Oh darling, how wonderful!' and then he addresses his little daughter, 'What shall we call you, little thing?' in a completely different and much higher voice. All this happens quite spontaneously and people who are interacting with a baby do not have to be taught how to do it. The important thing is that they should be in an environment which, because of its human warmth and friendliness, facilitates this kind of interaction. I believe that it is this, not silence or hushed voices, which provides the most appropriate setting for birth and the introduction of the newborn infant to life.

Leboyer also advises massaging the baby, something he does himself in his film *A Child is Born*, for a prolonged period of time while the mother lies and waits for her baby to be handed to her. Many women consider this an unnecessary and undesirable intrusion on the meeting of mother and child and would much prefer to be given their babies immediately. If the naked baby goes straight to the mother's arms she will touch her child in just the right way; she explores it, strokes the head and limbs, feels the plump firmness of its body, shapes and cradles the curves of cheeks, shoulders, buttocks. She starts with feathery, slight, tentative movements, touches the little clenched fist, traces the line of the brow, the curve of an ear, but soon proceeds to much bolder squeezing and embracing.

She is getting to know her baby through touch. This is not just something done to the baby for a therapeutic purpose but the beginning of the communication which will develop and continue for the rest of their lives together. It is part of a continuum and as such I believe that it is more important than any ritual performed on the baby by other people, however caring and however skilled.

Leboyer also teaches that the cord should not be clamped until it has stopped pulsating. Midwives have usually in the past waited for all available blood to be conveyed to the baby from the placenta before clamping it. It is only with the new high-speed deliveries which are becoming accepted as the norm in modern hospitals that doctors and midwives tend to clamp and cut immediately the baby is delivered.

R.D. Laing* believes that early clamping of the cord, before the baby has started breathing on its own, must cause trauma and asserts that in psychoanalysis he has encountered many suffering people who, when early childhood and infant memories are relived, recount a sudden shock and pain following birth which he connects with the cutting off of the blood supply to the newborn baby. All such experiences are remembered and stored in the organism, he believes, and the long-term results can be anxieties which affect cardiac rhythms and breathing function. Such events may underlie otherwise inexplicable allergies, upper respiratory tract infections, asthma and phobias of being in an enclosed space.

It would be very difficult to prove or to disprove psychological insights of this kind, but there is a strong case for so arranging birth and the introduction to life that the baby is not heedlessly exposed to unnecessary pain and shock. There is no reason why the first moment of living should be made an ordeal for the baby.

* Speaking to the British section of the International Society for Psychosomatic Medicine in Obstetrics and Gynaecology, October 1972.

Leboyer also recommends that the baby be put in a warm bath where it returns to the watery medium which it has just left and can begin to discover its own body and look around. The bath is the part of the welcome which hospital staff in Britain most criticize, suggesting that there is a real risk of hypothermia in the newborn unless it is warmly wrapped or put under a heater. Certainly newborn babies, especially tiny ones, can lose heat rapidly, and it is important that not only is the water comfortably warm to the elbow, but that the surrounding air in the room is warm and without draughts since the baby's greatest area of heat loss is the head, which is large compared with the rest of its body. Even in a modern hospital where the temperature in the delivery room is kept at an oppressively high degree, ventilation ducts may blow cold air over the baby. If the bath is to be given it must be placed well away from gusts of cold air and, since extra hot water cannot safely be introduced once the baby is in the bath, yet the temperature must be carefully controlled, it may be best for the bath to be lined with insulated material to retain the warmth. In fact, it is possible to use a box such as is sold for carrying picnic food and keeping it either hot or cold. This done, objections to the bath on the grounds that the baby might become dangerously chilled can be overridden.

In the Leboyer film it is Leboyer himself who baths the baby. There seems to be no reason why a doctor should be any more skilled at bathing a baby than the father or mother, and where the bath is done it is usually the father of the baby who takes over, with the help of a midwife who gives him confidence and emotional support. Fathers to whom I have talked who have done this have very much enjoyed it and have relished this first contact with their babies. Sometimes the mother has felt a bit out of it and longed to receive the baby back into her arms. In Julian Aston's film *Birth*, the mother waits expectantly, almost 'hovers', as she watches her husband bath their baby, and to the observer there seems a great space between the baby in the bath at the end of the bed and the mother craning her neck to see what is going on. One suggestion is for the bathing to be done right beside the mother's bed where she too can touch the baby and cradle it in the water.

From the father's point of view, giving the bath provides an opportunity for relating to the baby, which some men find difficult at first. Odent told me that he did not think the bath so necessary for the baby but that something important happened in the man. At Pithiviers I watched one man, who had wanted to dash off after the delivery to tell his mates, cradle his baby in the warm bath and as he did so the baby opened its eyes and looked straight at him; he looked down at his child and it seemed that in that moment a *father* was born.

But there are other questions about the Leboyer bath which express many women's sense of unease about the introduction of any ritual which interferes in their initial relationship with the newborn baby and deprives them of the chance to hold the child for as long as, and in any way, they wish. Women wonder whether the baby may not be equally comfortable and 'unfold' in the same way if it is simply left lying on the mother's body and whether skin contact may not be even more valuable than trying to recreate the conditions in the uterus which the baby has just left. Certainly the movements made by a baby resting on its mother's abdomen or breast are very similar to those of a baby in bath water, provided that the environment is peaceful and everyone allows time to stand still while the baby makes its first important discoveries about the world.

We need to review the culture of childbirth which we have come to accept as normal in our society and to create a new kind of birthing. Frédérick Leboyer has contributed something of inestimable value in directing our attention to the way in which we welcome our babies into the world and in reminding us of the importance of consideration and gentleness. He has raised important questions about how we greet the newborn and about the manner in which it is handled. But the answers we give to the questions he asks of us may well be different from those he provides himself, and the silent delivery and the ritual bath conducted by the doctor may not seem to us to provide the right environment for the birth for either the baby or the mother.

In becoming alert to the baby's needs it is easy to forget the woman who is bearing the child. The new concern with how the baby is treated at birth can be yet another way in which men tell women what they should do; another way in which 'experts' further sap our self-confidence.

It seems that Leboyer has little faith in the mother's ability to introduce her child to the world, resting it against her body and massaging it quite spontaneously with hands which reach out to hold it close and explore every tiny part. In fact, women do know what to do if they are *themselves* given love and support and a chance to hold their babies immediately. Provide the right environment for the mother, and the baby is greeted and touched and explored in just the right way.

But if the woman's emotional needs are neglected, if she feels she is merely the container from which the baby is removed, in spite of and not because of herself, she is unable to 'give' to her baby. If she finds herself in a loveless atmosphere, everything that is done to the baby, massage, bathing, music or whatever, is no more than ritual magic which fails to nourish the relationship between the mother and child that is just coming into being, which is what really matters in the all-important first hour after delivery.

It is women who bear the babies. The time has come for women to say exactly what they would like in childbirth. No cult should get in the way of a mother's first-hand experience of the baby she has just pushed out into the world.

This can apply as much to the cult of the ritual bath as to the technological cult at birth in what all too often looks like a well-equipped torture theatre. There is nothing to compare with giving birth without haste or cheer-leading among friends in an atmosphere of peace where the woman is encouraged, quite simply, to do whatever she *feels* like doing. Yet this, of course, is not the only reason why women should be able to choose the birth environment which they feel is right for them and to have loving people around them. Even if this contributed nothing to the mother–baby relationship, it ought to be so for the woman's sake. She is not just a baby-producing machine. She has her own needs – and her own rights as a human being.

The Baby Slips into Life

The newborn baby is a wonderfully constructed but often raw looking little creature, and not all mothers welcome their offspring with the delight which they think they ought to feel.

The slippery wine-red object slides out of the body screeching, wet, sticky, with a drop or two of blood on the forehead or in the matted hair, perhaps a white creamy substance – vernix – clinging to the skin, and bruises on the eyelids or between the eyes. The head has been moulded, like a ripe grapefruit, by its journey out of the uterus and down the birth canal, and the forehead slopes far back, like drawings of Neanderthal man. There may be a large blister or bump slightly to one side of the crown of the head where the baby was pressed down against an as yet incompletely dilated cervix.

The mouth may be a rosebud – or soft and wet like an old man's – and the hair abundant and frequently growing in extraordinary places as if nature had started off to make a monkey and then changed its mind, or sparse as if only the rudiments of humanity were being provided and the parents must make do with that.

The genitals seem extraordinarily large for such a small baby. The umbilical cord, jelly-like, white and blue, looks uncanny.

Before the child takes its first great gasp of air the body and face are often purplish-blue, the chest well caved in and the muscles slack. Then, with the inhaled air and the first animal-like cry or bleat, the lungs inflate and the baby may turn a brilliant red.

The baby clutches at the air with star-fish fingers and long arched feet, flexing and extending the limbs as air, cold, light and noise assail her, as the body at last slithers completely free from the confines of the uterus.

The kicking bundle the mother felt inside her is suddenly confronting her and demanding life – a being often unlike anything she imagined. It is not her, or a part of her, any longer, but aggressively *other*.

To the husband it may seem incomprehensible that this baby

– obviously a stranger to him – is also a stranger to her. This baby has lived nine months in her body. She has felt every kick and stretching movement. She has said – oh, so many times – 'His feet are just there, under my right ribs.' She has known when the baby slept and woke. And yet, after all this, she still confronts this creature with astonishment, and even with alarm.

Helene Deutsch points out that: '. . . In the last weeks of pregnancy . . . the relationship with the child is split: the being in the uterus already has his double, who is the subject of all expectations and fantasied wish fulfilments and whose real existence as a distinct person is gradually approaching . . . With the cutting of the physical umbilical cord . . . the mother receives a real substitute for what until then has been only a fantasy, an illusion.'*

In pregnancy the 'real' baby is the baby inside, and the baby that is to be is a shadow child. In the final weeks things change, and the baby about to be born becomes a larger, and even sometimes a menacing, shadow; what will it be like? Will it be normal? 'I have let myself feel soft and loving about it, allowed myself to be all wrapped up in dreams of the baby and in the comforting closeness of it during these waiting months, but . . . suppose it really is awful and I can't love it? Suppose I want nothing to do with it?' In the middle of the night the pregnant woman may wake and lie with half-formed thoughts like these floating in and out of her mind. There are thus two babies in her world – not one – right at the end of pregnancy: the baby that is kicking and squirming inside – felt as real, but still not really known – and the other fantasy child – the baby that is to be. And in the last weeks, and during labour, a woman is moving away from the first and inexorably towards her meeting with the second. Her willingness or unwillingness to do this may permeate her whole attitude to her labour. Part of the challenge of adapting to motherhood is to reconcile the fantasy with reality, and somehow to fuse these two babies into one. The task is to see that the optimum conditions are created for a mother to learn about her baby, and to let her idea of the baby-

* *Psychology of Women: Psychoanalytic Interpretation.* 2 vols. (Heinemann, 1944).

inside-her grow into and merge with the reality of the baby-in-her-arms.

All else – feeding the child and bathing and changing it, and knowing how to handle it – will then follow quite naturally. There will be trial and error and gradually a pattern of caring for the baby evolves, and the days which at first seem formless and full of feeds begin to have order in them again.

Meanwhile, the new mother looks at the baby's bright eyes, like a bird's, shining clear but not knowing her. The skin is creased like the crushed petals of a rose, but with fine down on it; she looks at the carefully delineated eyebrows, the shell-like fingernails, each separate stippled eyelash. The baby grips her finger, grasping on to life itself. It is born with this reflex to hang on, just as the monkey baby grips the mother's fur or the branch of a tree. It is the grasp which gave the Spartan baby a chance of life as it hung suspended over a precipice. It will fade, but just at the moment the newborn child clings to the mother.

And not only with his hand. If the baby's cheek is against the breast she may begin to root around for the nipple. Finding it, the tongue curls under the nipple, little jaws press firmly around both nipple and the brownish circle framing it, and the child starts to suck, as if with inbuilt knowledge that survival depends on the ability to do this. The sucking reflex of a healthy newborn baby who is put straight to the breast is often astonishingly strong. It is as if the child had been waiting for just this opportunity – had struggled to birth simply for this, and at last found a home. Even if not offered the breast, the baby may find fingers or thumb and suck as she has been sucking *in utero*.

For the woman, too, it is important that she has the chance to see, hear and handle her baby as much as she wants. It is not enough for the baby to be put down snug in a crib beside her. She needs to be able to touch and explore the child's body. If she is not given this opportunity she may lie feeling estranged from the child, uncertain even, especially if she drifts between sleep and waking after a difficult delivery, whether she has in fact given birth, or whether the child is still in her body, unconvinced of the baby's health and completeness, and rapidly losing confidence in her ability to be a mother. This happens particularly with premature babies or any newborn needing special care, when experts take over and the mother is left with her arms empty. When at last she is required to care for her baby she may be anxious and fearful, guilty at her own incapacity, and over-protective, a pattern of mothering which may persist in her relationship with the child for years afterwards.

Every mother needs extended time when she is alone with her baby and unselfconscious – not under the watchful eye of nurse or doctor – when she can quietly begin to get to know her baby, living in the here and now of close physical contact, safe from the proddings of what she should do, of how the baby 'ought to' behave. She need not perform any active caring function: it is enough simply that they are together. The father, too, benefits from this breathing-space. He does not have to prove that he can bath the baby, or change his nappy with all the professional skill of the sister who took the antenatal class; he should be able to hold the baby in his own way and enjoy his own kind of dexterity. If a man knows how to touch a woman tenderly he should be able to handle a baby. A woman has only to think of the pleasure her lover can give her, to realize that he has his own kind of sensitivity and gentleness.

In hospitals the father may be the man standing by the bed but he is rarely the man in it. If we had family rooms with large beds in which mother, father and baby could lie together in privacy, both parents could relate to the baby in their own way and at their own speed without the intervention of any rituals designed to 'ensure' bonding.

After the first few hours of life babies need something more than gentle handling, a peaceful environment and loving care; they benefit, like monkey babies, from stimulation – from being talked and sung to, rocked, rubbed and patted, and later still, being bounced and swung – and this the father is usually expert at doing.

To the new mother, who has, like the child, passed over the bridge of birth, and whose body is now empty of the newfound life, there may be no jubilation or explosion of happiness. And even though relatives and spectators may prod her to express the appropriate emotions, she may simply feel weary, achingly empty and lost, and unable to feel that the baby really belongs to her, or even that she wants it to.

This occurs particularly when the baby is taken from her to a nursery, and is not left close where she can explore it – not only with her eyes but with her fingers, checking that every part is there, stroking the soft down on his head, feeling the strength and vitality of the limbs, the mushroom-cushioned firmness of the little buttocks, the delicate whorls of the convoluted ears – which are somehow very obvious in a newborn baby and look as if they have something to reveal about its personality. 'It's Uncle Arthur's ears,' they say, or 'Lucy's feet,' as if every part must be traced to some other person's ownership, be accounted for – and the baby must be thus incorporated into the family, fixed to the tree of familial inheritance securely and for ever. The mother may start to look for these resemblances too, and then suddenly feel tired of the game and intensely irritated by it. This is *her baby*, and nothing like Emily or John or Granny.

But just now she may be looking at it with something approaching horror, both at its own appearance and strangeness, and her own reactions. For it looks like none of the pictures in the baby books she so assiduously studied, cuddly, smooth and scented with the special powder, shawl-swathed, firmly encased in the conventional wrapping of human dress. It is something outlandish and weird, its face bearing all the signs of senility rather than newness, scarlet as a boiled lobster, its shriek animal-like; it stops crying and she listens to the jerky, spasmodic breathing, the little sighs, grunts and starts, and not surprisingly, she does not feel that she is a 'born mother'. Her own reactions may alarm and depress her, making her afraid of her inner thoughts. She ought, she feels, to be overwhelmed with thanksgiving and love – and there is only this!

This is when she needs reassurance: that the love affair with the baby may be overwhelming the moment it is laid in her arms, may slowly dawn over the days following delivery – or hit her a week or so after the birth with all the immediacy and urgency of a first falling in love.

A mother needs time to get to know her baby just as we need time to get to know anybody else if an intimate and rewarding personal relationship is to grow. This knowledge does not come overnight. Much of the learning is informal, and unselfconscious, and is a result of noticing how other women handle their babies, or even how her own mother or an aunt handled a baby when she was a small girl herself, and of childhood play with dolls, or caring for animals or younger siblings. In different societies this handling is different, and the mother's spontaneous way of holding the child, settling it on her back or hip, in the fold of a shawl, or in a carry-cot or pram, and the way she washes it and feeds it, will reflect these actions of other women – which she has absorbed, and which have become part of her maternal behaviour. In peasant societies maternal behaviour tends to be unreflective and unintellectualized. The mother rarely questions her actions or pauses to think why, when or how she should perform a certain action. If the sociologist or other research worker stops her and questions this behaviour, I have seen how, in the West Indies, she either finds the query hilariously irrelevant or begins to lose self-confidence.

In modern Western society women seek to learn from the experts and start off with far less confidence than does the peasant mother. They only have to be told, 'Do it like this dear,' or 'Do you think he is getting enough milk from you?' to be assailed in a highly vulnerable spot. An anthropologist knows that there is no 'right' way of bathing a baby – only a great many fascinatingly different ways. In my classes I emphasize these cross-cultural aspects of child care and mothering, because it helps the new mother to be a little experimental in her approach to baby care. Her basic task is to learn from the child, rather than to superimpose techniques which she has acquired from a book or from watching a demonstration. The baby has not read the books, however good they are. Learning to be a parent means learning from the child.

I realized when I read through these labour reports that the mothers writing in these pages do not report on feelings of horror when they first see their babies. Most insist that they are absolutely beautiful. This is a pity in a way, because it makes them all seem 'natural mothers', whereas I am sure they were not. Perhaps the fact that in childbirth classes they talked a good deal about maternal (and paternal) feelings, the appearance of the new baby, and the mother-child relationship in its less positive as well as its immediately rewarding aspects, meant that these women were not shocked by the baby, or their own reactions to it.

But they do make it clear that they felt the need to touch and explore their babies and to feed them when they cried. Various mothers reported verbally that they ran into difficulties when they tried to conform to a rigid feeding schedule demanded by the hospital. Many hospitals have abandoned schedules on the postnatal ward, but understaffing, or lack of flexibility in care of mother and baby, mean that women find themselves in a situation of conflict. If this occurs, early discharge seems the sensible thing when possible, and the woman can insist on this.

When a baby is removed to the nursery to be watched for a couple of days after a forceps delivery or a Caesarean section, a mother faces special problems of relating to her baby, and may harbour anxious fears about it and her capacity as a mother.

The more a woman feels unable to cope, the more urgent is her need to get to know the infant, and the more she should be encouraged to have the baby in the vicinity, so that when she feels ready she can do things for it. If someone else takes over she is only confirmed in her feelings that she is inadequate as a mother. This is equally true of women suffering from mental breakdown after childbirth, as experience at the Cassell Hospital has shown. Babies are amazingly tough, and stand up to unskilled handling and flourish on it. Only thus can the mother gradually grow in confidence, understanding – and tenderness.

Some of the mothers having second babies whose stories are told here had been through this with the first, and talked about their feelings in class. These women often needed extra support after the baby was born, and when this was given were able to breastfeed their second babies successfully.

Once the baby is delivered, existence outside the warmth and comfort of its mother's body is in some ways a continuation of life in the uterus. Although the break appears sudden and dramatic, caring for the baby and answering its needs require conditions which echo that of intrauterine life. The baby is one of the most helpless of newly delivered creatures, unable like a baby kangaroo to burrow inside its mother's pouch, or to struggle to its feet and follow its mother like a foal. In its nakedness it seems about as vulnerable as a new-hatched baby bird.

In the uterus the baby was comfortably warm, rocked in the cradle of the pelvis as the mother moved, near her heart, and, since the fetus is known to respond to sound, able to hear her heart-beats (and also the sound-effects of digestive machinery!) It was fed without effort on its part, kept clean in the amniotic fluid, able to move and exercise within a limited area and protected from infection. It was the placenta, the baby's 'tree of life', which performed many of these functions involving nutrition and getting rid of waste material, and when the baby is born the mother takes over the work of the placenta and the other organs which automatically cared for her baby.

Most of the problems that crop up in the early weeks reflect a mother's – or someone else's – inability to respond sensitively to the baby's needs, and as far as possible to recreate initially the conditions of life in the uterus. Sometimes adults are determined, on the contrary, to make the infant 'fit in' – to socialize and train it before it is ready to learn. The result is usually a great waste of energy, and in the first few months the baby is either 'broken', or starts fighting the mother, and they both get embroiled in a conflict about feeding or sleeping.

All babies cry, at least sometimes – on average, it has been estimated, about two hours a day. This usually means they need feeding, perhaps holding and cuddling. But some babies cry anyway. Try turning the wireless on or doing some vacuum cleaning near by. It is impossible to make a baby sleep, but it is often easier for the baby to sink into sleep if you have a background of rhythmic sound which, perhaps because it is closer to the conditions the baby experienced inside the uterus, may have a more soporific effect than complete silence. Any household machine, music, or a background of human conversation can do this. It may be the origin of the lullaby, which uses the frequencies of the human voice combined with a rhythmic and musical cadence. Parents can make and adapt their own lullabies and it does not matter if they are nonsense.*

Babies who cry a great deal, often for hours every evening

* *The Experience of Breastfeeding*, Sheila Kitzinger (Penguin, 1987).

are said to have 'three month colic' or 'paroxysmal fussing'. This does not mean that the mother is inadequate or is doing anything wrong, but the baby is obviously claiming more attention, and needs it, and it is an effective way to let adults realize that she is lonely and needs to be cuddled. Sometimes these babies are getting their food fast, but need much more sucking time. The answer may be a dummy. It is doubtful whether wind is the reason, although a crying baby will produce wind simply because he has inhaled air while crying; it is the effect rather than the cause.

There are on the market various types of papoose sling which enable the father or mother to carry the baby around, rather as an African mother quite naturally does. The closeness and the jogging movement often make the baby much happier. If the worst comes to the worst the frantic parents can get in the car and drive the baby round, as most babies adore motoring and immediately fall asleep, only to wake and cry whenever the car stops at traffic lights.

One of the things over which the modern woman can get most fraught is how, when and on what to feed the baby. It is as if nutrition epitomizes motherhood, and as if her capacity to be a good mother is dependent on her ability to get sufficient milk into the baby, through the processes of digestion, and the waste products out the other end, without mishap. To a man this emphasis on the nutritional and excretory may seem overdramatized and inexplicable. But for a woman who is unsure of herself as a mother it symbolizes the weight of responsibility that she has taken on for this new life, this utterly dependent baby.

The middle-class mother in our society today is the one most likely to want to breastfeed, but even though she may be determined to show that she can do it, this determination cannot by itself produce milk, and is in fact not a good basis for the relaxed and casual feeding which is the dominant pattern all over the world where breast-feeding is most successful. Whereas she no longer believes that intercourse involves merely her tacit acceptance of male advances, then lying still and thinking of England, attitudes to breastfeeding are still infused with notions about clocks and timing, about getting the wind up, and even with pseudo-hygienic practices involving washing nipples with soap and water before and after feeds. Any woman who really wants to can breastfeed (with the very rare exception) and she probably would if she were alone on a desert island and left to experiment and work it out for herself.*

Whereas it is usually safe to bottlefeed, the safest method of all is to breastfeed – not only because the baby is far less likely to get gastro-enteritis, and because there is the occasional allergy to cow's milk, but for other reasons: a baby is more likely to be immune to various illnesses its mother has had if breastfed; he can absorb the calcium in his mother's milk much more easily than in cow's milk (very low calcium can lead to tetany); and breast milk has five times the amount of Vitamin C as *unboiled* cow's milk. Of course, most of these disadvantages can be remedied by adding things to cow's milk, and the bottlefed infant thrives. But again and again we see how, as we move farther away from the natural and spontaneous, we run into dangers and take risks which science and technology can only elaborately and painstakingly counteract by yet new inventions which, whilst solving some problems, at the same time produce new dangers and risks. And in all this it is often human relationships that suffer.

The spontaneous movement and sounds that a mother makes as she rocks or talks nonsense to her baby – apparently meaningless and without pattern – are vital factors in the development of a relationship between the mother and baby, and, because this is the primal human relationship, between the child and society. Breastfeeding can be important because it involves a special sort of touch, flesh contact, and an acceptance of the child by the mother as it returns to her body – a sort of physical loving which can be just as significant for the baby and mother as the physical expression of adult love. For breastfeeding is a sexual activity (one reason perhaps, why some women hate it), and part of the very wide spectrum of sexuality in a woman's life, ranging all the way from her image of herself as a woman, through making love and the process of childbearing, to the different ways in which she deals with her sons and

* *The Experience of Breastfeeding*, op. cit., p. 202

204

daughters as they grow up through childhood and adolescence, and her reactions to menstruation and to the menopause.

Most women who want to breast-feed welcome support from their partners who may have to shield them from the advice that comes from other people about what they ought and ought not to do. The let-down reflex, which occurs when milk is released from the glands into the ducts, ready to pour out through tiny holes in the nipple (rather like the holes in the rose of a watering can), is closely associated with the emotions. A woman hearing a baby cry, whether or not it is her own, may feel the breasts start to tingle, and is immediately ready to give milk. On the other hand if she is feeding peacefully, and someone she dislikes, or with whom she has a strained relationship, comes into the room, the milk supply may be suddenly inhibited.

The nearest analogy to favourable conditions for the new mother to learn how to breastfeed is that provided by what are commonly considered favourable conditions for love-making: a comfortable warm bed, privacy, a relaxed atmosphere, and a sense of timeless leisure. And just as with intercourse, the first attempts may not bring the delight or satisfaction which was hoped for, so gradually the nursing couple, like the couple making love, learn to understand and respond to each other's needs; for breastfeeding, and indeed the whole of parenthood, is – like any form of loving – a process of discovery.

Difficulties in establishing or maintaining breastfeeding can mean that a woman feels a failure almost from the start, and that she gets involved in a struggle with the baby which may persist long after infancy.

On the other hand, the decision to breastfeed cannot, in itself, guarantee the child's, or the mother's, placidity. Often in the early post-natal days latent anxieties come to the surface, and a perfectly 'normal' and apparently contented woman can wonder, as she holds the baby in the bath, what would happen if she tilted her arm just a little and let the baby's head sink under the water (and be a little tempted to do it); or when the child cries and she seems to be able to do nothing to comfort it, she can have the impulse to escape – to rush out of the house and leave her tormentor. She can find herself weeping unaccountably, or tense and alert as if always listening for the least sound from the baby.

A feeling of let-down after childbirth is common, especially on about the third or fourth post-partum day – the sort of depression that can follow any big event in one's life, or a party, or the end of the exams. It often only lasts for a day, and is experienced more often in the alien atmosphere of hospital than after a home birth. It is no good saying 'snap out of it', and it is much better for a woman to simply ride out the lethargy that accompanies despondency, or the tears that can be the outward sign of a storm of despair. A partner can offer a good deal of quiet emotional support by asserting confidence in her as a mother, and love for her as a woman.

Sometimes, however, the mother and baby relationship seems to break down completely – a woman rejects her child (maybe weeks after the birth) – and this is usually a sign of more serious post-natal depression, for which expert help should be sought. The new mother may feel the baby is not really hers, or hate him and try to harm him, be completely unable to face the responsibility of motherhood, and at the same time feel guilty about this. This sort of depression does not come like a bolt out of the blue. It happens to women who have known periods of severe depression before, or who frequently experience violent mood swings, and who have very often had a very unstable and unhappy childhood. Sometimes there has been no mother, and sometimes a very possessive, domineering one who has taken over her daughter's life, and lived through her, so that she feels she has no identity of her own, and no right to be a mother herself. Either way, she can be a very frightened woman when confronted with the demands of motherhood. She expresses this by disclaiming the responsibility through paranoid feelings that other people are out to take the baby away from her or to destroy it, or by an utter disregard of the child, as if it did not exist, or overt aggression towards it. If a couple face this sort of problem it is essential that they seek help, and are not ashamed to do so. Even severe mental illness of this type can be treated, and there are many women who went through a period, sometimes of many months, of complete irrationality and confusion who are now living useful, positive lives.

But although the new mother is the one who gets most

attention, all is not necessarily plain sailing for the new father, and it is important to realize that he, too, may have some major emotional adjustments to make – not only in accepting added responsibility, but also in sharing love. In some societies (as for example one Amazonian Indian tribe in South America) the husband climbs into the hammock and enacts the birth instead of the wife, whilst she quietly slips away into the bush and has her baby without assistance. In some cultures the 'lying in' is the husband's prerogative, and the woman gets back to cooking the porridge, doing the washing, and caring for her man and other children, whilst he lies in bed. Rituals of this type, collectively known as 'the couvade', imply that childbirth involves such change that the accompanying emotional and social transition can be helped by a visual enacting of the drama – a formalized pattern of behaviour which is marked off and completely different from the normal, everyday one and which represents values important to the society. In some cultures the couvade is a means of making a public statement that this man is really the father of this child. Let there be no doubt about it. Look what he is going through! The couvade may have different meanings in each one. But its very existence points to a situation of stress. In Britain psychoanalysts have examined the 'couvade syndrome' in expectant fathers – toothache, tummy-ache, loss of appetite, backache and morning sickness, and even mental illness – and reported that about 11% of all expectant fathers have some symptoms of psychogenic origin in relation to their wives' pregnancies.

But what of afterwards too? The arrival of a new baby brings extra and obvious, stresses, including broken nights, a great deal of dirty washing, extreme difficulty in planning ahead about anything, because the baby is paramount, a kind of formless unfolding of time – and *things* around everywhere – hairbrushes, rubber sheets, plastic ducks, cots and carrycots, bottles of antiseptic and pots of baby cream. Having a baby usually means accumulating a vast array of equipment (unless the parents are able to resist the advertisements) which is all waiting to be bumped into or tripped over. Many a man feels that the baby has taken over and is the most important member of the family, when he takes it for granted that *he* should be.

The new mother may have little time for anything or anybody else, and when a man is jealous this seems to provide painfully obvious evidence that she no longer loves him. The baby becomes a rival in the home, an ever-present one who loudly proclaims his presence. Many men start off on fatherhood insecure, lacking in confidence and immature. They are not ready to accept responsibility and they hope that life can continue more or less as before. All too often a woman finds herself with two babies in the home. A man who has experienced emotional deprivation – real or imagined – in his childhood, or who has never really solved the fundamental problems of jealousy (perhaps because he has never had any brothers or sisters and has always been the apple of his parents' eyes, or because he was protected from ever knowing that these violent feelings existed in himself) may still have to work out emotions about the baby which others have coped with earlier in their lives.

For in many ways the battles and problems of a sexual relationship and parenthood are a continuation of other, earlier conflicts and the struggle for identity as we move through childhood and adolescence.

Yet these usually merely repeat patterns laid down by their own parents. Having a baby gives a man and woman a chance to reassess themselves and their relationship. We have most of us grown up in families where the woman and the children are treated as the property of the man, where he is head of the household, where his main function is seen in the world of work outside the home, where the woman is expected to serve his needs and those of the children, bears the whole burden of nurturing and is supposed to find complete fulfilment in being 'a good wife and mother'. The process of becoming a parent provides a challenge to create new forms of relationships, new forms of the family, in which there can be genuine shared parenting and in which each partner can develop their full potential.

Helpful Organizations

National Childbirth Trust
9 Queensborough Terrace
Bayswater
London W2 3TB
Tel: 01 221 3833

Association for Improvement in Maternity Services (AIMS)
163 Liverpool Road
London N1 0RF
Tel: 01 278 5628
Please send SAE *for information*

Active Birth Centre
55 Dartmouth Park Road
London NW5
Tel: 01 267 3006

Association of Radical Midwives
62 Greetby Hill
Ormskirk
Lancashire L39 2DT

Independent Midwives' Association
65 Mount Nod Road
Streatham
London SW16 2LP

Society to Support Home Confinements
Lydgate
Lydgate Lane
Wolsingham
Weardale
Co. Durham DL13 3HA
Tel: 0388 528044

Glossary of Terms Used in Childbirth

This is far from being an exhaustive list and consists solely of terms women are likely to meet during pregnancy and labour. I have included, however, phrases and words other than those appearing in the text, because it may be useful for expectant parents to understand the terms and abbreviations likely to be used in their hearing. Many of those terms concern abnormalities – because when things are going well it seems that it is not so necessary to give them verbal description!

Every woman has a right to know what is taking place in and to her body, and what she can do to help. This means that she also needs to understand some of the things that can go wrong, an essential preliminary if she is to appreciate help that she is offered. It is worse than useless to think that by keeping a woman in ignorance she will not worry, or that information about her own inside and the child she is bearing has nothing to do with her. Knowledge really can cast out fear but it must be knowledge not only of pathological conditions and nature's errors, but of what can constructively be done in the situation which presents itself.

Terms are described here not so much as they would be relevant to the obstetrician, but as they relate to the women's personal experience of antenatal procedures and labour.

ACIDOSIS   The building up of acid products in the body, with resulting chemical imbalance. Ketones may be discovered in the blood and urine during a very long and tiring labour, and the woman is often given a glucose drip as a pick-me-up. In fact, if a woman is allowed to eat during labour and does not go a long time without food this is unlikely to happen. Some hospitals insist on women having nothing by mouth in case they have to have general anaesthesia and may vomit and inhale stomach contents. General anaesthesia is rarely necessary nowadays as an epidural can be given instead.

ADDUCTOR   The muscle running along the inside of the upper leg.

ALBUMIN   Protein which appears in the urine. It can be a sign of pre-eclampsia (which see).

AMNIOTIC FLUID   The liquid in which the baby is floating in the bag of waters inside the uterus.

AMNIOSCOPE   An instrument which examines the fluid around the baby by shining a minute light through the cervix in front of the baby's head.

ANOXIC   Deprived of oxygen.

ANTERIOR   At the front. Usually in obstetrics means towards the mother's front.

ANTERIOR LIP   A part of the cervix still gripping the baby's head. This corresponds to transition (which see). It is a time when great patience is needed, and when the mother welcomes emotional support and encouragement.

APGAR RATING   A quick and simple way of estimating a baby's health and responsiveness to the challenge of living based on the observation of the baby's reflexes, muscle tone and breathing. It is carried out at one and five minutes after birth. Ten is full marks. Invented by Dr Veronica Apgar.

APH   Ante-partum haemorrhage. Bleeding before delivery, or before labour begins (i.e. more than at the beginning of a period). The best thing is to ring the doctor or hospital, and go to bed or go into the hospital immediately.

AREOLA   The darker coloured circle around the nipple.

ARM   Artificial rupture of the membranes. The doctor nicks the bag of waters (which has no nerve endings, so it does not hurt) to start off or to speed up labour. It is usually an unnecessary intervention which may lead to further interventions, and is best avoided.

ATTITUDE   The posture of the baby in the uterus e.g. curled up, only partly curled up, or stretched out.

BRAXTON-HICKS   'Practice' contractions of the uterus felt at any time from the seventh month of pregnancy. At first noticed as brief, isolated bouts of activity, these contractions often later become regular and can be confused with true labour.

BREECH   The baby's buttocks in the cervix instead of the head. An extended or frank breech is one in which the baby's legs are stretched out, with the feet somewhere about the shoulders. A flexed breech is one in which the baby is curled up in a ball.

CEPHALO-PELVIC DISPROPORTION (CPD)   The baby's head cannot progress through the cavity of the mother's pelvis, with resulting delay in labour. It is often given as the reason for doing a Caesarean section when there is no clear evidence of CPD, only that labour is taking a long time.

CERVIX   The neck of the uterus, which hangs down in the vagina like a clapper of a bell, and thins out and then dilates during labour.

COLOSTRUM   The first liquid produced by the breast in late pregnancy and following delivery. It contains gammaglobulin, which may supply antibodies for the baby, and is very high in protein (6% as compared with 1% protein in milk). It is the baby's natural first food.

CONTINUOUS FETAL MONITORING   (see Fetal Heart Monitor)

CONTRACTION   The shortening and thickening of a bundle of fibres when a muscle is working. In uterine contractions the longitudinal muscles are pulled up, so opening the circular muscle fibres looped like a coiled spring around the cervix.

CRESCENT   A lip of cervix still round a part of the baby's head (see Anterior Lip).

DEEP TRANSVERSE ARREST   This occurs in cases of posterior presentation (which see) when the baby's head becomes wedged in the hollow of the sacrum, and is unable to flex further. Forceps, or a vacuum extractor (which see), are often used to effect delivery.

DISPROPORTION   A situation in which it looks as if the baby may be too big or too oddly positioned to pass through the mother's pelvis with ease. It is difficult to be certain about this until a woman is well into labour and the uterus has had a chance to show what it can do.

DRIP   Glucose or a hormone solution is gradually dripped through a bottle down a long tube and through a fine needle into a vein of a hand or arm. This is fixed on with sticky tape, and left until after the baby is born. Apart from the initial prick, it does not hurt.

EDD   Estimated date of delivery. Labour may be a couple of weeks before or after this date. First babies tend to come a little bit later than second and subsequent babies.

EFFACEMENT   The thinning out of the walls of the cervix until the cervix is drawn up into the main body of the uterus. This precedes labour proper, and often overlaps with the first phases of dilatation.

EMBRYO   The baby in the uterus in the first three months of pregnancy.

ENDOMETRIUM   The lining of the uterus.

ENDORPHINS   Natural painkillers which are produced when we are under stress or engaged in any physically demanding action.

ENDOSCOPE   An instrument which measures the acidity of the baby's blood. It can be used after the membranes have ruptured. A drop of the baby's blood is sucked out through a tiny prick in the scalp, and the results are known in five minutes.

ENGAGED   The biggest part of the baby's head is deep in the mother's pelvis, like an egg in an eggcup. This often occurs in the last weeks of pregnancy, but sometimes not until labour is under way.

ENGORGEMENT   Often when the milk is first secreted, on about the third day after birth, the breasts become swollen, hard and hot. This can be relieved by cold compresses and by putting the baby to the breast. It soon settles down if the baby is fed whenever he wants to be.

EPIDURAL   An injection in the space around the spine which causes loss of sensation from the waist down. The amount of movement lost varies with the anaesthetic used. Uterine action is slowed for the first 10 minutes, but in a difficult labour the uterus may relax better between contractions, thus improving its blood supply. The mother does not want to bear down and the bladder must be emptied by catheter. Forceps are often necessary for delivery. As the injection is topped up – through a tube left in place – the mother may not have movement of her legs for about two hours after delivery.

EPISIOTOMY   A cut in the perineum to speed delivery.

EXTENSION   Any part of the baby which is stretched out, for example when there is an extended arm, the baby's arm is stretched out and may be slowing up labour.

FALLOPIAN TUBES   The tubes branching out from either side of the uterus in which fertilization takes place.

FETAL BLOOD SAMPLING   A technique of taking blood from the baby's scalp through the dilating cervix to estimate its pH – the balance between acid and alkaline in the blood. If there are concerns about the fetal heart rate and Caesarean section is proposed, this should be done before any definite decision is made about Caesarean section as fetal heart rate recording alone is unreliable.

FETAL DISTRESS   The baby being short of oxygen while still inside the mother. Signs are a very fast heart rate, above 160 beats per minute (tachycardia) followed by very slow heart rate – below 90–100 beats per minute (bradycardia) and/or late decelerations (type II dips) when the heart rate remains slow after a contraction is finished. A more definite diagnosis can be made if a suspicious heart rate recording is followed by fetal blood sampling (which see).

FH   Fetal heart. On the case sheet this may be ticked after about the sixth month to indicate that it has been heard, and later in pregnancy the actual rate of the baby's heart is recorded, as it also is in labour. The normal limits of the fetal heart rate are between 160 and 120 a minute.

FETAL HEART MONITOR   A machine which records the baby's heart by the means of electrodes placed on the mother's abdomen over the spot where the heart is located or by clipping or screwing an electrode into the baby's scalp while it is still inside the mother.

FETUS   The baby in the uterus from the third month until delivery.

FLEXION   Any part of the baby may be curled up. Usually the baby is completely flexed during the larger part of labour.

FONTANELLE   The soft spot on the baby's head.

FORAMEN OVALE   The opening between right and left atrium of the baby's heart, which closes after birth.

FORE WATERS   The liquor (which see) in front of the baby's head.

FULL DILATATION   or 'fully'. The condition of the cervix when it is open to about the size of the palm of a large hand, including the thumb joint. This is approximately ten centimetres. It marks the end of the first stage of labour and may be followed immediately by the urge to push or by a transitional phase during which contractions feel weaker and further apart and the woman can take some rest.

FULL TERM   About 40 weeks from the first day of the last period.

FUNDUS   The upper part of the uterus.

GA   General anaesthesia. The patient loses consciousness.

GAS AND OXYGEN   This is offered by mask towards the end of the first stage when and if contractions are painful, and can be self-administered. It should be taken with contractions only.

GLUTEI   Buttock muscles.

GRAVID   Pregnant. A primagravida is a woman who is in her first pregnancy, a multigravida one who is in her second or subsequent pregnancy.

HAEMOGLOBIN   H-b. The part of the blood which carries oxygen around the body. High haemoglobin means that there is ample iron present in the blood to do this. A low haemoglobin means that there is insufficient iron. Because a pregnant woman has a greater volume of blood the iron concentration is lower than when she is not pregnant and at the end of pregnancy is 35 per cent below the non-pregnant level. This is normal and does not mean that she requires iron supplementation.

HIND WATERS   The liquor (which see) behind the baby's head.

HYPEREMISIS   Persistent vomiting in pregnancy.

HYPERTENSION   Raised blood-pressure. This can be one sign of pre-eclampsia (which see).

HYPERVENTILATION   Chemical imbalance in the blood resulting from the flushing out of carbon dioxide by over-breathing – typically, forceful heavy breathing.

INCO-ORDINATE UTERINE ACTION   A disharmony in the muscles of the uterus. This produces strong contractions which fail to dilate the cervix.

INDUCTION   Helping labour to start artificially with an ARM (which see) and Syntocinon drip (see drip) or Prostin pessaries. There was an epidemic of inductions in the early seventies, but rates have now fallen. The practice of routine induction on the grounds that a woman is ten days or two weeks past her EDD is unjustified. You do not need to agree to induction unless you are given very good reasons and have had time to think it over. Induced labours tend to be longer and to result in more forceps deliveries and Caesarean sections. Women have more drugs for pain relief and the Apgar scores (which see) of the babies tend to be lower.

INERTIA Insufficient uterine activity. Primary inertia means weak contractions from the beginning of labour. Secondary inertia means a weakening or complete cessation of uterine contractions before the baby is delivered.

INVOLUTION The return of the uterus almost to its pre-pregnancy size and weight – from about 2 lb after delivery to about 2 oz. Breast-feeding assists this process.

JAUNDICE About a third of new-born babies go a bit yellow between the second and fifth days of life. This is even more likely if they are premature. It is called 'physiological jaundice', and there is no cause for concern. Sometimes, however, babies are jaundiced (and this usually happens within 24 hours of delivery), signalling that something is wrong, and this may be associated with rhesus incompatibility (which see). Jaundice is treated with light (phototherapy).

KETOSIS Imbalance of blood chemicals resulting from the burning of fat. It results in vomiting, drowsiness and over-breathing, and the woman's breath smells of new-mown hay.

LET-DOWN REFLEX A conditioned reflex stimulated by the feeling of the baby at the breast or his cries, or even simply thinking about feeding the baby. When it occurs the breasts tingle and feel warm, the nipples become erect, and the milk is secreted into the ducts.

LEVATOR ANI Muscles of the pelvic floor, round the vagina, urethra and anus, which support all the pelvic contents, and down through which the baby is born.

LIQUOR The waters in which the baby floats in the uterus. Also called the amniotic fluid.

LITHOTOMY A delivery position in which a woman lies on her back with her legs raised, wide apart and supported by stirrups. Convenient for the doctor, often difficult and painful for the woman giving birth.

LOCHIA   Discharge after childbirth – at first red for a few days, then pink, and finally colourless.

LOW FORCEPS   Delivery of the baby with forceps when the head is already on the perineum (which see).

MECONIUM   The first contents of the baby's bowel. A dark, greenish-black sticky substance.

MEMBRANES   The bag of waters.

MID-STREAM SPECIMEN   A specimen of urine acquired halfway through emptying the bladder by stopping passing water through contracting the pelvic floor muscles strongly, and then continuing into a container.

MOULDING   The shaping of the baby's head by his passage down the birth canal.

MUCOUS PLUG   (see *Show*)

MULTIPARA   A woman who is bearing her second or a subsequent child. A grand-multipara is a woman who has already had four babies.

OCCIPUT   The crown of the baby's head. Left occipito-anterior (LOA) is a position in which the baby is lying on the mother's left looking towards her back – the commonest presentation. Right occiputo-anterior (ROA) is one in which the baby is lying on the mother's right looking towards her back.

O'DRISCOLL LABOUR METHOD   A method of active management in which the uterus is stimulated by intravenous oxytocin if it looks as though labour is going to take longer than 12 hours.

OEDEMA   Fluid retained in the tissues causing puffiness. It may be a sign of pre-eclampsia (which see). Usually it occurs in the legs simply because the mother is hot and tired.

OESTROGEN   An ovarian hormone. It maintains the growth and activity of the uterus during pregnancy, helps the mother's breasts to develop for breast-feeding, and makes connective tissues more flexible, the pelvic joints mobile, and the cervix soft. After birth it causes milk to be secreted into the ducts.

OVARIES   The female egg cell 'factory' and storage house situated at the end of the fallopian tubes (which see).

OVULATION   The time when the egg cell ripens – normally about half-way between two periods.

PALPATION   Feeling the position of the baby through the abdominal wall.

PARACERVICAL A pain-killing injection given around the cervix.

PARIETAL The bones fitting like a cap and forming the top of the skull. In the new-born baby they are separated by a suture running from back to front, and this means that, as the baby's head is pressed down through the birth canal, it is moulded and the parietal bones can move slightly towards each other.

PARTOGRAM A chart of the progress of labour measured against a statistical norm for dilatation of the cervix, descent of the fetal head, and length of the second stage.

PELVIC FLOOR The muscles around the vagina, urethra and anus which support the bladder and uterus, and down through which the baby is born.

PELVIS The bony framework within which the baby lies. The front is formed by the pubic symphisis, and the back by the sacrum.

PERINEAL MASSAGE A method of stroking and stretching with warm oil the lower inside vagina and the area between vagina and anus.

PERINEUM The soft tissue on the outside around the vagina and anus. These stretch and fan out with the descent of the baby's head, and open up with a warm, tingling sensation when the head is 'on the perineum'.

PETHIDINE A drug given by injection to a woman in labour, often at about two-thirds dilatation of the cervix, which takes the edge off pain and makes her drowsy. Normally given in 50 mg doses, a 'baby' dose being 50 mg., and the standard dose 100 mg. It can result in the mother feeling very drunk and out of control.

PLACENTA The after-birth. It is through the placenta that the baby is nourished and receives his oxygen from the mother's bloodstream, and through it, too, he excretes waste products. The placenta has been called 'the tree of life' for the baby. It is constructed like a sponge, with blood filling the spaces. The mother's blood does not actually mix with the baby's blood, but is separated from it by a thin membrane. The placenta looks like a large piece of raw liver.

PLACENTA PRAEVIA The placenta is situated in the lower part of the uterus. When the cervix dilates, the placenta which lies over the part which is being 'taken up' starts to peel off, and this results in bleeding, commonly from the 28th week of pregnancy. This should be taken as a warning sign, and the hospital or GP rung immediately. A soft-tissue x-ray may be used in diagnosis, and a Caesarean section may be the best course of action.

POSTERIOR   Towards the back. A posterior presentation is a baby lying with the crown of the head at the mother's back so that he is facing her front. This is also known as 'face to pubis'. Most posterior presentations are on the mother's right hand side – right occipito-posterior (ROP), although some are on the left, a left occipito-posterior (LOP). In these cases the baby's head tends to be less well flexed than with anterior presentations (which see), and a larger diameter of the baby's head is coming through the cervix and birth canal. Frequently there is delay as the baby's head is pressed against the mother's sacrum. A woman expecting labour with a posterior should be prepared for a long first stage with backache. A persistent occipito-posterior (POP) is one in which the baby's head does not rotate into the anterior, and in which the baby is delivered looking up towards the mother instead of down towards the bed.

POSTMATURE   It is very easy to be uncertain about one's dates, and no-one knows what constitutes post-maturity. But on the whole the baby more than two weeks overdue may not be receiving an adequate blood flow through the, by this time, rather elderly placenta, and the doctor will often advise inducing labour.

PR   Per rectum. A rectal examination.

PRECIPITATE LABOUR   Very rapid labour – under five hours in a woman having her first baby. There are also precipitate first and second stages.

PRE-ECLAMPSIA   Toxaemia of pregnancy. Symtoms are: raised blood pressure, albumin in the urine, puffiness of the fingers, ankles and legs, and a sudden excessive weight gain. Treatment is rest and sedation, including – very important – peace of mind, and sometimes starting labour off a little before the baby is due.

PREMATURE   or low birth weight. An international classification consisting of any babies under 2,500 g. Many Chinese and Indian babies weigh less and are full term, and this is then a better guide to whether the baby needs extra care.

PREPARATION   'Prepping'. The woman's blood-pressure is taken, the midwife brings the case history up to date and listens to the baby's heart. She checks its position, and the woman has a shower. Perineal hair does not need to be shaved, and the practice has now largely been abandoned. Nor is it necessary to have a enema or suppositories to empty the lower bowel unless the woman is constipated, and this practice has also largely fallen into disuse.

PRESENTATION   A description of the way in which the baby is lying in terms of that part of the baby which is down in the cervix. The most common is a vertex presentation (which see).

PRIMIPARA   A woman having her first baby.

PROGESTERONE   An ovarian hormone which is manufactured by the placenta in pregnancy.

PROLAPSE   Slackness in the pelvic floor muscles, which allow the bladder or uterus to drop down, with resultant low backache and stress incontinence (which see). Parts of the vaginal wall can also prolapse when there has been excessive straining in the second stage. Mild prolapse can often be helped by regular pelvic floor exercises.

PROSTIN   Prostaglandin pessaries which soften the cervix and induce labour.

PSYCHOPROPHYLAXIS   This has come to be used as a general term for any modern and systematic method of preparation for childbirth. Strictly speaking, however, it has a more specific meaning: a method of training, which historically stems from work done in the USSR and France, based on Pavlovian theories of conditioned reflex behaviour and including 'disassociation' techniques. The term is used in the latter sense in these pages.

PUDENDAL BLOC   An injection around the vagina which anaesthetizes the birth outlet. This can be done before a forceps delivery and before an episiotomy (which see).

PUERPERIUM   The six weeks after childbirth when the mother's body is returning to its pre-pregnancy state. A post-natal examination takes place at the end of this time.

PV   Per vaginam. A vaginal examination.

PYELITIS   A kidney infection. It starts with shivering and an acute pain, often on the right side, nausea or vomiting, a headache, and a sudden rise in temperature. It may occur in mid-pregnancy or after a difficult birth. With treatment it usually soon clears up.

QUICKENING   The time when the mother first feels the baby's movements. This is usually between 16 weeks (with a woman who has had a baby, and knows what the flutterings are) and 20 weeks. If you are uncertain of when the baby is due, 22 weeks from quickening will give you an approximate date.

RECTAL EXAMINATION   An examination through the rectum.

REGIONAL ANAESTHESIA   An anaesthetic which removes sensation from only one part of the body and which is given by injection.

RHESUS   All blood is either rhesus positive (i.e. contains an agglutinating factor found in the rhesus monkey) or rhesus negative. (85% of human blood is positive.) If the baby is positive and the mother negative, the mother may form an antibody to the baby's blood, a bit like an allergic reaction. So blood of all expectant mothers is tested. The detailed genetic make-up of the father is also important in determining whether or not the child is likely to trigger off a reaction in the mother's blood. It is rare for the baby to be affected in the first pregnancy (unless the mother has been previously sensitized). Many Rh negative women never become sensitized at all. Haemolytic disease (haemolytic jaundice) is most likely to affect the fourth or subsequent baby of an Rh negative mother who is married to an Rh positive man who carries *both* pairs of Rh genes (that is, he is homozygous). Nowadays the Rh negative women is given an injection after the first delivery – depending on the baby's blood group – which ensures that she will not become sensitized in later pregnancies.

ROOTING   The reflex, with which the baby is born, to hunt around for the nipple.

RUBELLA   German measles.

SACRUM   The large bone which forms the back of the pelvis.

Sacro-iliac pain is pain in the small of the back.

SECOND STAGE OF LABOUR   The active expulsive stage. This may begin at full dilatation, but there is often a lull of 20 minutes or more before there is a compelling urge to push. Sometimes, when there is an anterior lip, the woman wants to push and thinks she must be in the second stage before it has really started, and it is best for her to continue to breathe rhythmically and avoid pushing as much as possible until the urge is overwhelming.

SEGMENT   The upper part of the uterus is that part around the baby's body. The lower segment, that part around the baby's head.

SHIRODKAR SUTURE   A stitch around the cervix sometimes done if there is a risk of miscarriage in mid-pregnancy.

SHOW   A blood-stained mucous discharge which often heralds the start of labour, but may take place several days before labour actually commences. It is the plug from the cervix, and frequently there is no more show as labour progresses.

SPINAL   An injection into the spine causing complete paralysis of the lower part of the body. There is no bearing down sensation. There may be a bad headache afterwards.

SPONTANEOUS DELIVERY   The mother giving birth to the baby herself, without mechanical assistance from her attendants.

STRESS INCONTINENCE   Wetting your pants when you cough or laugh because the pelvic floor muscles are weak.

STRIAE   Stretch marks. The skin stretches from underneath, so it is not much help to rub oil except to keep the upper layer of skin supple.

SUTURING   Sewing up.

TEST FEEDING   Weighing the baby before and after a feed in the same clothes. Not a good idea unless the baby is obviously ill, since it tends to increase the mother's anxiety and disturb the baby.

THIRD STAGE OF LABOUR   From the birth of the baby to the delivery of the afterbirth.

TENS   Transcutaneous Electronic Nerve Stimulation. Pads containing electrodes are placed on certain parts of the back and produce a pulsed buzzing when the woman presses a switch.

TOXAEMIA   (see pre-eclampsia).

TRANSITION   The very end of the first stage of labour, when a tiny part of the cervix – called the 'lip' – is around the baby's head. It is often the most difficult part of labour, but may last for only a few contractions.

TRANSVERSE LIE   The baby lies across the uterus. If labour is allowed to continue this may be a shoulder presentation, and it can result in obstructed labour, so the doctor turns the baby.

TRIAL OF LABOUR   The term is used when there is some evidence of possible disproportion (which see) or other signs that labour may not be straightforward, so the obstetrician decides to see what the uterus can do, whilst having everything ready for a Caesarean section if necessary.

TYPE II DIPS   Slowing of the fetal heart after the contraction has finished. In the interval between contractions the heart rate should return to normal. If it does not, this is an indication that the baby may be under too much stress.

ULTRASOUND SCAN   A method of visualizing the baby inside the uterus by means of ultrasonic waves. These sound waves bounce off solid objects to produce a picture on a screen like a TV set. Though there is no evidence of risk with the use of ultrasound it should only be used when there is a definite reason for doing so, since no research has been able to prove that it is 100 per cent safe.

UMBILICAL CORD   The cord which connects the baby and placenta is about 20 inches long, consists of two arteries and one vein, and is covered with a jelly-like substance which makes it difficult for it to get knotted, especially as it is floating in liqour (which see).

VACUUM EXTRACTION   A method of sucking the baby out by means of a cup attached to the fetal scalp. This is rarely used in Britain but has taken the place of forceps in Scandinavia, and is probably a safer and gentler method of assisted delivery.

VACUUM EXTRACTOR   An instrument which applies suction to the baby's head and draws it down the birth canal, like a vacuum cleaner. It is most effective used with a conscious woman who can bear down at the same time as suction is applied. Also called a 'ventouse'.

VAGINAL EXAMINATION   Examination through the vagina.

VERNIX   The creamy substance, like cottage cheese, which protects the baby's skin, and which comes off gradually after birth. It is formed from sebum from the sebaceous glands and epidermal cells.

VERSION   Turning the baby. For example, the doctor may turn a breech (which see) into a vertex (which see) by holding the baby's head and buttocks through the mother's abdominal wall and moving the baby round in the direction of its nose. It may be tried after the 32nd week of pregnancy. It is important for the woman to relax well.

VERTEX   The top of the baby's head when still inside the mother (see Presentation).

WALLER'S SHIELDS   Plastic domes with a hole in the middle for the nipple, worn under the bra in late pregnancy to help retracted nipples stick out. In fact, if the mother can get the baby well fixed on the breast, with part of the aureola as well as the nipple drawn into the baby's mouth, the baby will do the work of shaping the nipples better than any device that can be worn.